ORIGO
STEPPING STONES

2.0

COMPREHENSIVE MATHEMATICS

S0-ARL-038

AUTHORS

James Burnett
Calvin Irons
Peter Stowasser
Allan Turton

PROGRAM CONSULTANTS

Diana Lambdin
Frank Lester, Jr.
Kit Norris

CONTRIBUTING WRITERS

Debi DePaul
Beth Lewis

STUDENT BOOK A

ORIGO
EDUCATION

INTRODUCTION

ORIGO STEPPING STONES 2.0 STUDENT JOURNAL

ORIGO Stepping Stones 2.0 is a world-class comprehensive program, developed by a team of experts to provide a balanced approach to teach and learn mathematics. The Student Journal consists of two parts — Book A and Book B. Book A comprises Modules 1 to 6, and Book B Modules 7 to 12. Each book has Lesson and Practice pages, a complete Contents, Student Glossary, and Teacher Index.

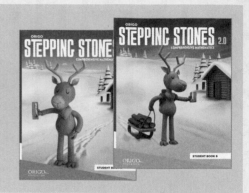

LESSON PAGES

There are two pages for each of the 12 lessons in every module. This sample shows the key components.

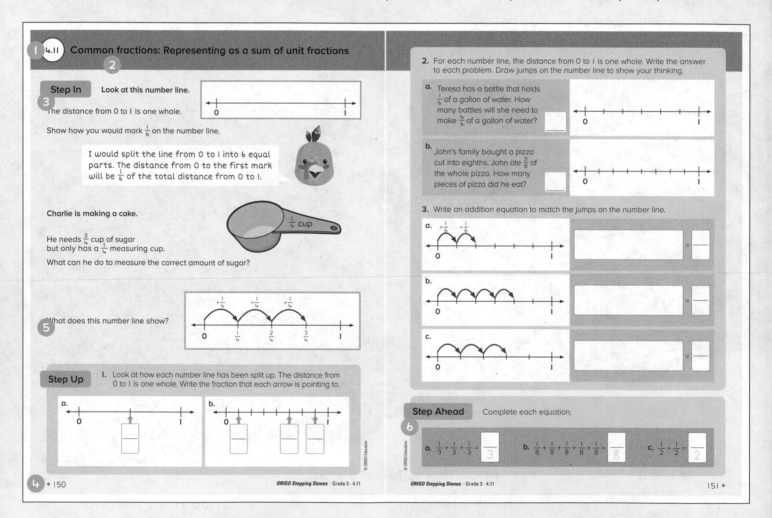

1. Module number and Lesson number.

2. The lesson title tells the content of the lesson. It has two parts: the stem (or big idea) and the leaf (which gives more details).

3. The Step In is designed to generate classroom discourse. Open questions are posed to make students think about different methods or answers.

4. For Grade 3, Book A shows a blue diamond beside each page number and index references are in blue. Book B shows a green diamond and index references are in green.

5. Step Up provides appropriate written work for the student.

6. The Step Ahead puts a twist on each lesson to develop higher order thinking skills.

PRACTICE PAGES

Lessons 2, 4, 6, 8, 10, and 12 each provide two pages for maintaining concepts and skills. These samples show the key components.

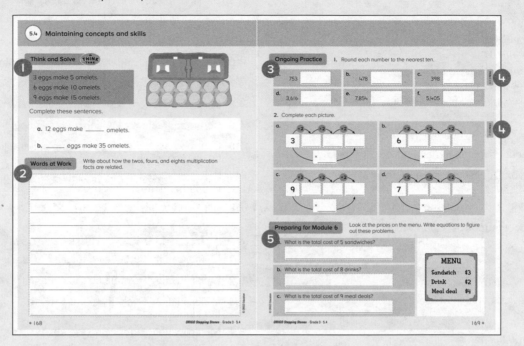

① The *ORIGO Think Tanks* are a popular way for students to practice problem-solving. There are three Think Tank problems in each module.

② The development of written language is essential. These activities aim to help students develop their academic vocabulary and provide opportunities for students to write their thinking.

③ Ongoing Practice relates to content previously learned. Question 1 always revisits content from a previous module, and Question 2 revisits content from this module.

④ This tab shows the original lesson.

⑤ Each right-hand page provides content that prepares students for the next module.

⑥ Regular written practice of mental strategies is essential. There are three computation practice pages that focus on specific strategies in each module.

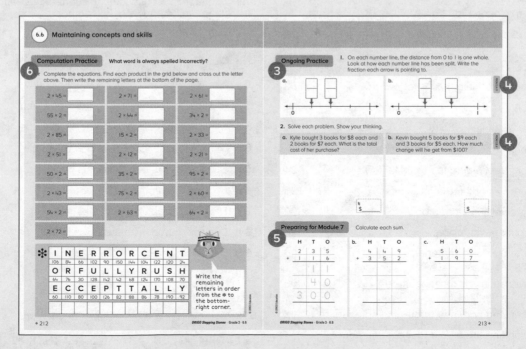

CONTENTS

BOOK A

MODULE 1

1.1	Number: Writing three-digit numerals and number names	6
1.2	Number: Identifying three-digit numbers on a number line	8
1.3	Number: Representing four-digit numbers	12
1.4	Number: Writing four-digit numerals and number names	14
1.5	Number: Writing four-digit numbers in expanded form	18
1.6	Number: Locating four-digit numbers on a number line	20
1.7	Multiplication: Introducing the symbol	24
1.8	Multiplication: Using the turnaround idea with arrays	26
1.9	Multiplication: Doubling and halving multiples of ten and five	30
1.10	Multiplication: Introducing the tens facts	32
1.11	Multiplication: Introducing the fives facts	36
1.12	Multiplication: Reinforcing the tens and fives facts	38

MODULE 2

2.1	Addition: Investigating patterns	44
2.2	Addition: Two-digit numbers (with composing)	46
2.3	Addition: Two- and three-digit numbers (with composing)	50
2.4	Addition: Developing written methods	52
2.5	Addition: Solving word problems	56
2.6	Time: Reading and writing to the minute	58
2.7	Time: Relating past and to the hour	62
2.8	Time: Reading times in different ways	64
2.9	Time: Measuring intervals in minutes	68
2.10	2D shapes: Exploring rectangles	70
2.11	2D shapes: Exploring rhombuses	74
2.12	2D shapes: Exploring relationships between shapes	76

MODULE 3

3.1	Multiplication: Introducing the twos facts	82
3.2	Multiplication: Reinforcing the twos facts	84
3.3	Multiplication: Extending the twos facts	88
3.4	Multiplication: Introducing the fours facts	90
3.5	Multiplication: Reinforcing the fours facts	94
3.6	Multiplication: Extending the fours facts	96
3.7	Multiplication: Solving word problems	100
3.8	Number: Working with place value	102
3.9	Number: Comparing and ordering three-digit numbers	106
3.10	Number: Comparing and ordering three- and four-digit numbers	108
3.11	Number: Rounding two- and three-digit numbers	112
3.12	Number: Rounding three- and four-digit numbers	114

MODULE 4

4.1	Division: Introducing the symbol	120
4.2	Division: Connecting multiplication and division	122
4.3	Division: Introducing the tens facts	126
4.4	Division: Introducing the fives facts	128
4.5	Division: Reinforcing the tens and fives facts	132
4.6	Division: Introducing the twos and fours facts	134
4.7	Division: Reinforcing the twos and fours facts	138
4.8	Common fractions: Reviewing unit fractions	140
4.9	Common fractions: Writing with symbols	144
4.10	Common fractions: Representing unit fractions on a number line	146
4.11	Common fractions: Representing as a sum of unit fractions	150
4.12	Common fractions: Relating models	152

MODULE 5

5.1	Multiplication: Introducing the eights facts	158
5.2	Multiplication: Reinforcing the eights facts	160
5.3	Multiplication: Exploring patterns with the eights facts	164
5.4	Multiplication: Introducing the ones facts	166
5.5	Multiplication: Introducing the zeros facts	170
5.6	Multiplication: Reinforcing the ones and zeros facts	172
5.7	Multiplication: Solving word problems	176
5.8	Subtraction: Counting back to subtract two-digit numbers (with decomposing)	178
5.9	Subtraction: Counting back to subtract two- and three-digit numbers (with decomposing)	182
5.10	Subtraction: Counting on to subtract two-digit numbers (with composing)	184
5.11	Subtraction: Counting on to subtract two- and three-digit numbers (with composing)	188
5.12	Subtraction: Solving word problems	190

MODULE 6

6.1	Multiplication: Introducing the nines facts	196
6.2	Multiplication: Reinforcing the nines facts	198
6.3	Multiplication: Exploring patterns with the nines facts	202
6.4	Multiplication: Solving word problems	204
6.5	Division: Introducing the eights facts	208
6.6	Division: Reinforcing the eights facts	210
6.7	Division: Introducing the ones facts	214
6.8	Division: Introducing the zeros facts	216
6.9	Data: Working with many-to-one picture graphs	220
6.10	Data: Working with bar graphs	222
6.11	Data: Working with line plots	226
6.12	Data: Working with line plots (fractions)	228

STUDENT GLOSSARY AND TEACHER INDEX — 234

CONTENTS

BOOK B

MODULE 7

7.1	Multiplication: Introducing the sixes facts	244
7.2	Multiplication: Reinforcing the sixes facts	246
7.3	Multiplication: Introducing the last facts	250
7.4	Multiplication: Working with all facts	252
7.5	Multiplication: Solving word problems	256
7.6	Addition: Making estimates	258
7.7	Addition: Introducing the standard algorithm	262
7.8	Addition: Working with the standard algorithm (composing tens)	264
7.9	Addition: Working with the standard algorithm (composing hundreds)	268
7.10	Addition: Using the standard algorithm with three-digit numbers	270
7.11	Addition: Introducing the compensation strategy	274
7.12	Addition: Solving word problems	276

MODULE 8

8.1	Division: Introducing the nines facts	282
8.2	Division: Reinforcing the nines facts	284
8.3	Division: Introducing the sixes and last facts	288
8.4	Division: Reinforcing the sixes and last facts	290
8.5	Common fractions: Counting beyond one whole	294
8.6	Common fractions: Exploring improper fractions	296
8.7	Common fractions: Identifying improper fractions on a number line	300
8.8	Common fractions: Exploring equivalent fractions	302
8.9	Common fractions: Identifying equivalent fractions on a number line	306
8.10	Capacity: Reviewing liters and fractions of a liter	308
8.11	Mass: Reviewing kilograms and introducing fractions of a kilogram (grams)	312
8.12	Mass/capacity: Solving word problems	314

MODULE 9

9.1	Subtraction: Making estimates	320
9.2	Subtraction: Introducing the standard algorithm	322
9.3	Subtraction: Using the standard algorithm with two-digit numbers (decomposing tens)	326
9.4	Subtraction: Using the standard algorithm with three-digit numbers (decomposing tens)	328
9.5	Subtraction: Using the standard algorithm with three-digit numbers (decomposing hundreds)	332
9.6	Subtraction: Exploring subtraction involving zero	334
9.7	Subtraction: Applying the compensation strategy	338
9.8	Common fractions: Comparing unit fractions (length model)	340
9.9	Common fractions: Comparing unit fractions (number line)	344
9.10	Common fractions: Making comparisons with the same denominator (number line)	346
9.11	Common fractions: Making comparisons with the same numerator (number line)	350
9.12	Common fractions: Solving comparison word problems	352

MODULE 10

10.1	Area: Calculating the area of rectangles (customary units)	358
10.2	Area: Calculating the area of rectangles (metric units)	360
10.3	Area: Using multiplication to calculate area	364
10.4	Area: Identifying dimensions of rectangles	366
10.5	Area: Decomposing composite shapes to calculate area	370
10.6	Area: Solving word problems	372
10.7	Multiplication: Extending known facts	376
10.8	Multiplication: Using the distributive property with two-digit numbers (partial products)	378
10.9	Multiplication: Using the associative property with two-digit numbers (double and halve)	382
10.10	Algebra: Investigating order with multiple operations	384
10.11	Algebra: Solving problems involving multiple operations	388
10.12	Algebra: Writing equations to match two-step word problems	390

MODULE 11

11.1	Number: Building a picture of 10,000	396
11.2	Number: Representing five-digit numbers	398
11.3	Number: Writing five-digit numbers in expanded form	402
11.4	Number: Comparing and ordering five-digit numbers	404
11.5	Number: Rounding five-digit numbers	408
11.6	Number: Reinforcing rounding with five-digit numbers	410
11.7	Money: Adding amounts in cents (bridging dollars)	414
11.8	Money: Working with dollars and cents	416
11.9	Money: Calculating change (cents)	420
11.10	Capacity: Reviewing cups, pints, and quarts	422
11.11	Capacity: Introducing gallons	426
11.12	Capacity: Solving word problems	428

MODULE 12

12.1	Division: Two-digit numbers	434
12.2	Division: Two-digit numbers (with regrouping)	436
12.3	Division: Thinking multiplication to divide two-digit numbers	440
12.4	Division: Making estimates	442
12.5	Division: Reinforcing the think-multiplication strategy	446
12.6	Angles: Comparing using non-standard units	448
12.7	Angles: Measuring as fractions	452
12.8	3D objects: Identifying prisms	454
12.9	3D objects: Comparing prisms and pyramids	458
12.10	Perimeter: Introducing perimeter	460
12.11	Perimeter: Exploring the relationship with area	464
12.12	Perimeter/area: Solving word problems	466

STUDENT GLOSSARY AND TEACHER INDEX   472

Step In | Look at these mix-and-match cards.

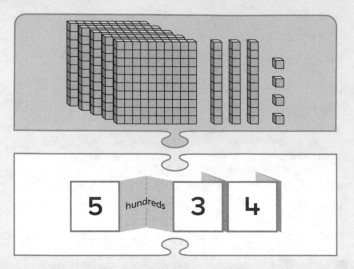
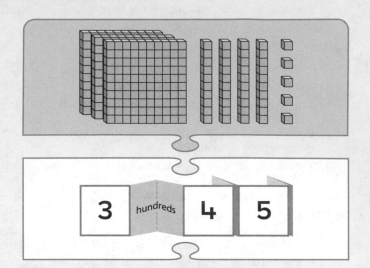

What is the value of the 5 in each block picture? What is the value of each 3?
How can you figure out which cards match?

Complete the third card in each set by writing each number name.

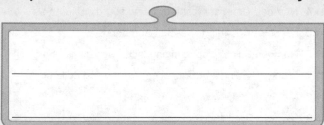
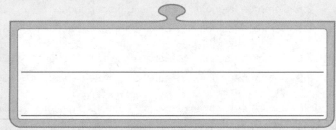

Step Up | 1. Look at the blocks. Write the matching number on the expander. Then write the number name.

a.

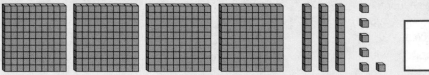

b.

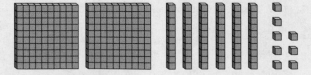

2. Write the matching numeral. Then write the number name.

a.

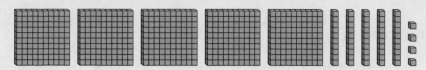

_____

b.

_____

c.

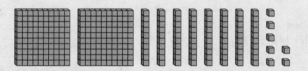

_____

d.

_____

Step Ahead   **a.** Look at these blocks. Write the matching number name.

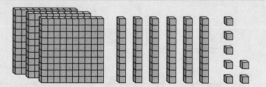 

_____

b. Add one more block to each place and write the new number name.

_____

Step In   Look at this number line.

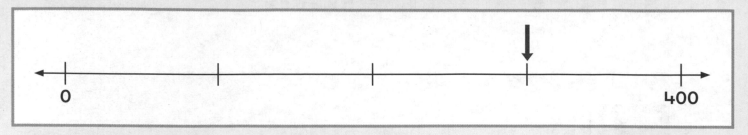

0   400

What number would you write in the position shown by the arrow? How do you know?

How could you show the position of 150 on the number line?

What other numbers could you label on the number line?

> You could split the part between 0 and 100 into 10 smaller parts that are the same length. The first part would be 10.

Estimate the position of 230 on the number line.

Step Up   I.   Write the number that should be in the position shown by each arrow.

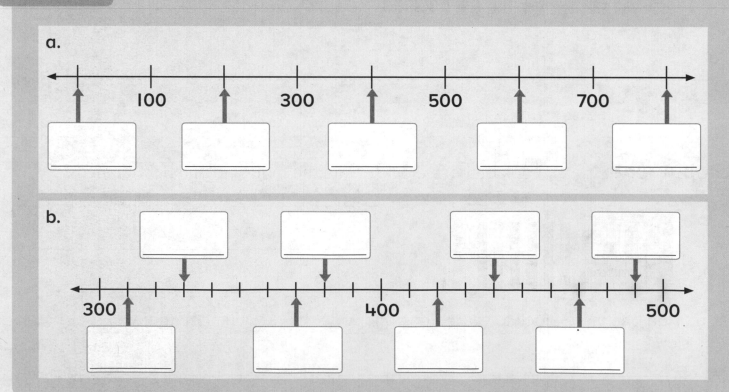

a.

100   300   500   700

b.

300   400   500

2. Write the number for each arrow. Think carefully before you write.

a.

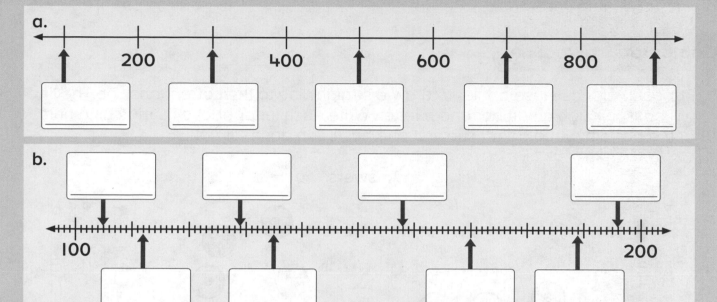

b.

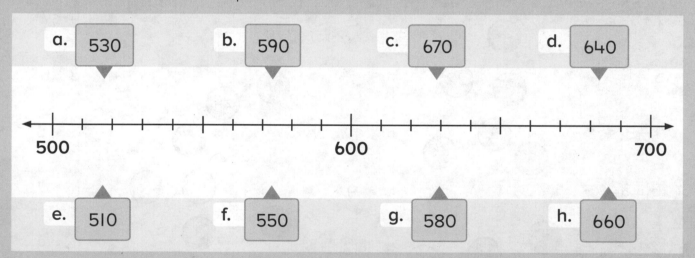

3. Draw a line to show the position of each number.

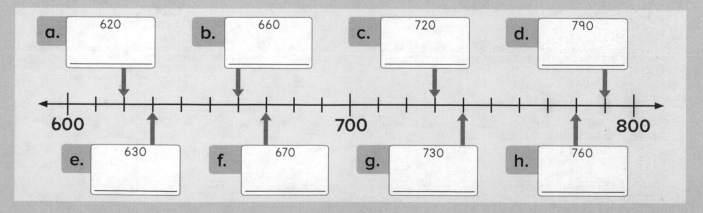

Step Ahead

Callum has made some mistakes on his number line. Find each mistake and write the correct number.

a. 620   **b.** 660   **c.** 720   **d.** 790

600   700   800

e. 630   **f.** 670   **g.** 730   **h.** 760

© ORIGO Education

Computation Practice

★ For each of these, use a ruler to draw a straight line to the correct answer. The line will pass through a number and a letter. Write each letter above its matching number at the bottom of the page. The first one has been done for you.

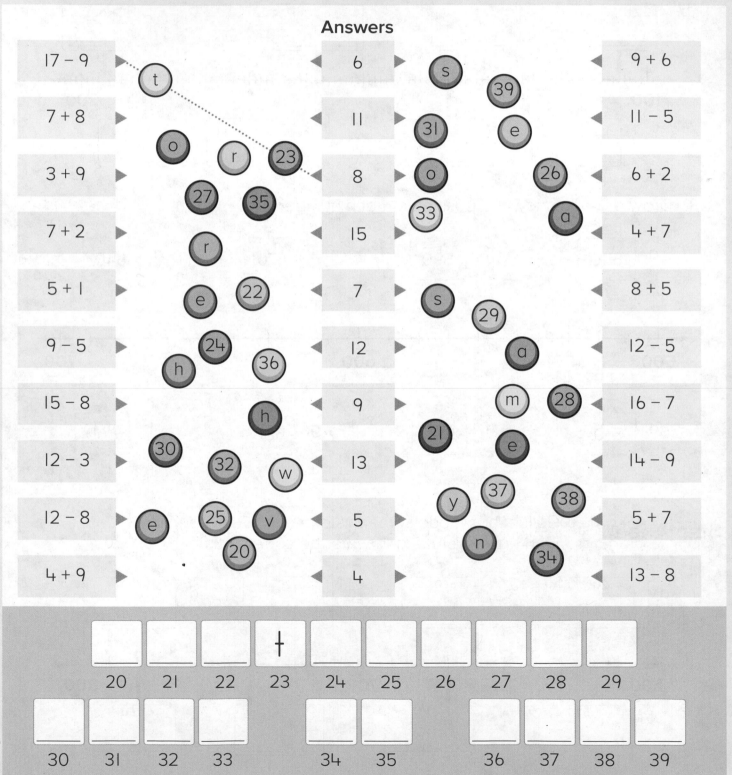

Ongoing Practice

1. Write **less than**, **equal to**, or **more than** to describe the mass of the fruit compared to one pound.

a.

_____ 1 pound

b.

_____ 1 pound

2. Look at the blocks. Write the matching number on the expander. Then write the number name.

a.

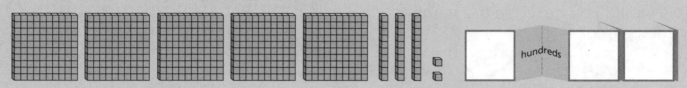

hundreds

_____

b.

hundreds

_____

Preparing for Module 2

Write the totals. Use patterns to help.

a.

13 + 2 = _____

23 + 2 = _____

33 + 2 = _____

53 + 2 = _____

b.

26 + 3 = _____

36 + 3 = _____

46 + 3 = _____

66 + 3 = _____

c.

31 + 1 = _____

41 + 1 = _____

51 + 1 = _____

81 + 1 = _____

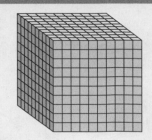

Step In   What do you know about this block?

If you regrouped this block as hundreds blocks, how many of them would you get?

How many tens blocks would you get? How many ones blocks would you get?

Are there more than or fewer than 1,000 books in your library?

Are there more than or fewer than 1,000 pages in a big dictionary?

Look at this picture of blocks.

How would you describe the number in each place?

Write numbers in the place-value chart to match the blocks.

Show how you would record the same number on the expander.

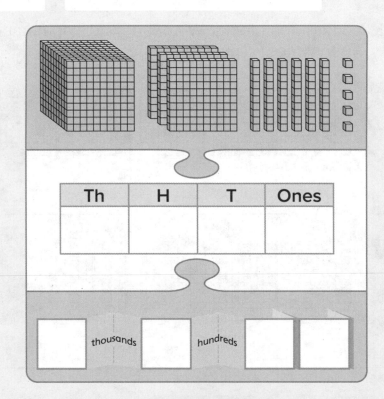

Th	H	T	Ones

thousands   hundreds

Step Up   1. Write numbers in the place-value chart to match the blocks.

a.
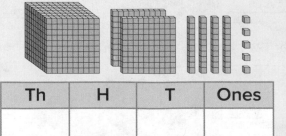

Th	H	T	Ones

b.
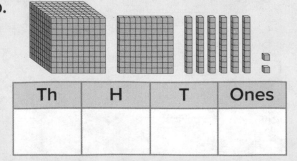

Th	H	T	Ones

2. Look at the blocks. Write the matching number on the expander.

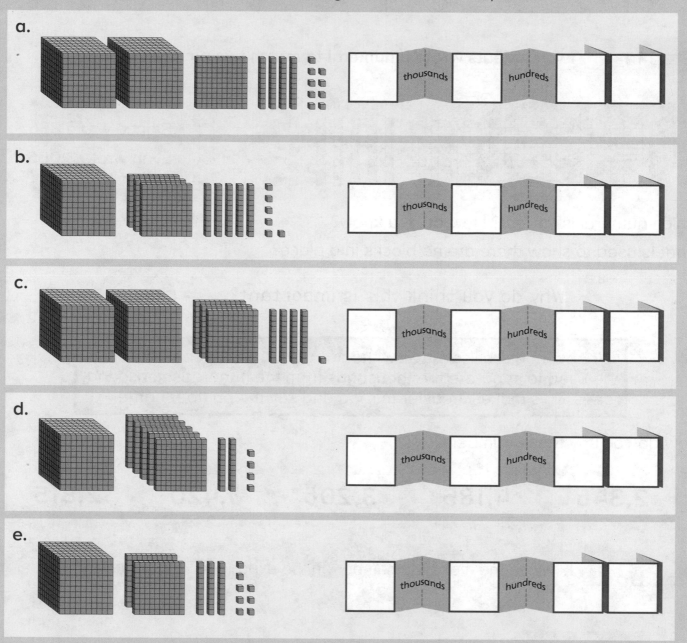

Step Ahead These blocks have been moved around.
Write the matching number on the expander.

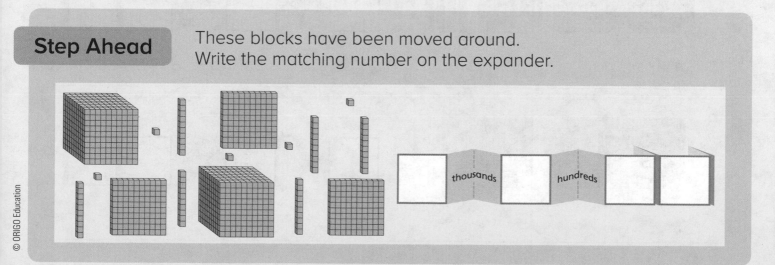

© ORIGO Education

Step In

Two students wrote a numeral to match this picture of blocks.

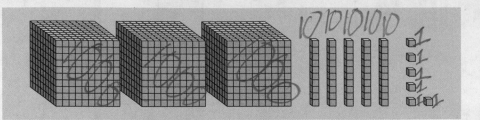

Bianca wrote **356**.
Evan wrote **3,056**.

Which numeral is correct? How do you know?

What is used to show there are no blocks in a place?

Why do you think this is important?

When a numeral is written without an expander, a comma can be used to separate the thousands from the hundreds, tens, and ones. This makes it easier to read and say the number name.

How do you say these numbers?

| 2,346 | 4,185 | 3,206 | 7,420 | 2,815 |

Step Up

1. Write the matching number on the expander. Then write the number in words.

a.

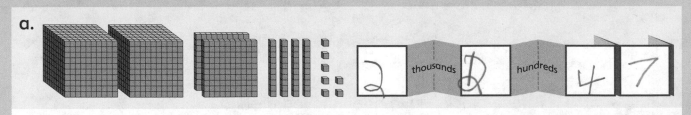

b.

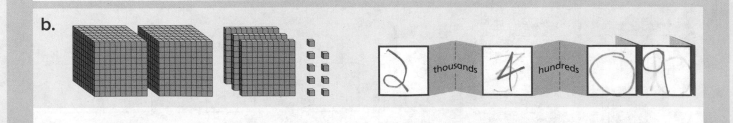

2. Write the matching number on the expander. Then write the number name.

a.

4,819

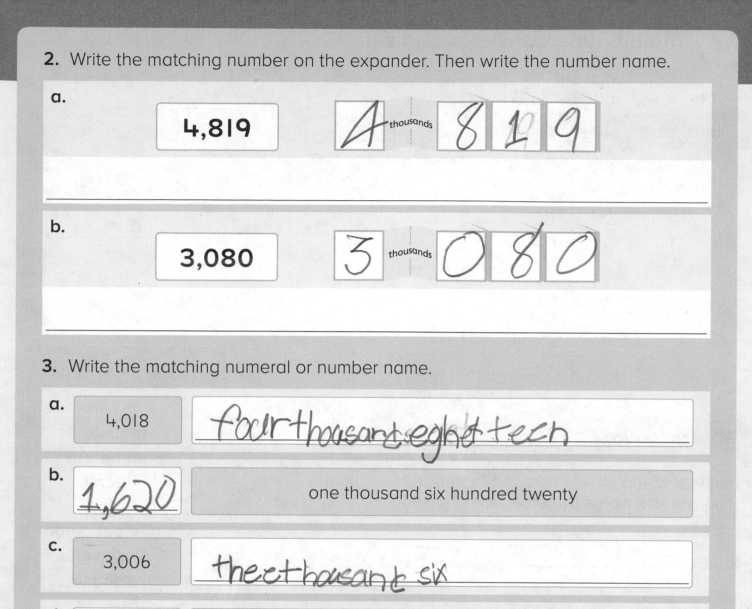

4 thousands 8 1 9

b.

3,080

3 thousands 0 8 0

3. Write the matching numeral or number name.

a.

4,018

fourthousand eghteen

b.

1,620

one thousand six hundred twenty

c.

3,006

theethousant six

d.

2,915

two thousand nine hundred fifteen

Step Ahead

The ancient Greeks placed pebbles in grooves to show numbers. This board shows the number 3,109.

a. What do the grooves on the board show?

numbers

b. What do the pebbles show?

3,109

c. What does it mean if there are no pebbles in a groove?

no numbers

Think and Solve

The numbers on the lines are the totals of the numbers in the circles.

For example, A + C = 11.

A = ☐

B = ☐

C = ☐

D = ☐

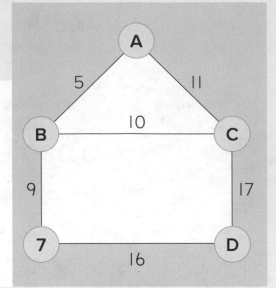

Words at Work

Write a numeral that has four digits.

Write how you could show your number.
You can use words from the list to help you.

| thousands |
| hundreds |
| tens |
| ones |
| number name |
| place value |
| comma |

Ongoing Practice

1. Write **less than**, **equal to**, or **more than** to describe the mass of the fruit compared to one kilogram.

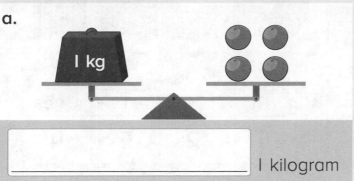

a.

_____ I kilogram

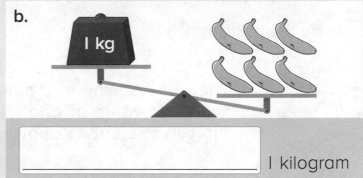

b.

_____ I kilogram

2. Write the number for each arrow. Think carefully before you write.

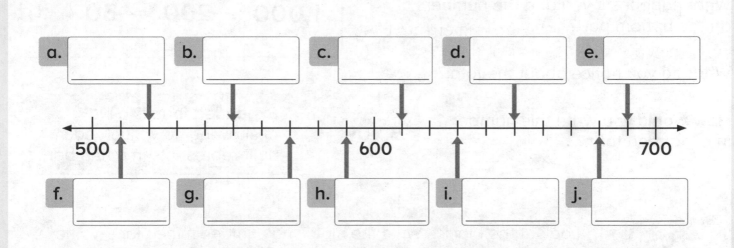

a. _____ b. _____ c. _____ d. _____ e. _____

500   600   700

f. _____ g. _____ h. _____ i. _____ j. _____

Preparing for Module 2

Write the number of hundreds, tens, and ones. Then write an equation to show the total.

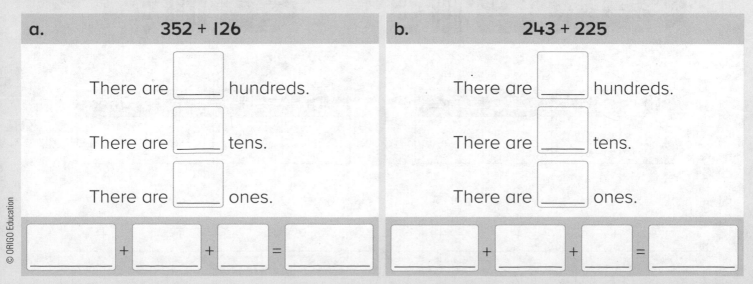

a. 352 + 126

There are ____ hundreds.

There are ____ tens.

There are ____ ones.

____ + ____ + ____ = ____

b. 243 + 225

There are ____ hundreds.

There are ____ tens.

There are ____ ones.

____ + ____ + ____ = ____

Step In

What number is shown on each part of this mix-and-match card?

Why do the parts match?

The part at the bottom tells the value of each digit in the chart above.

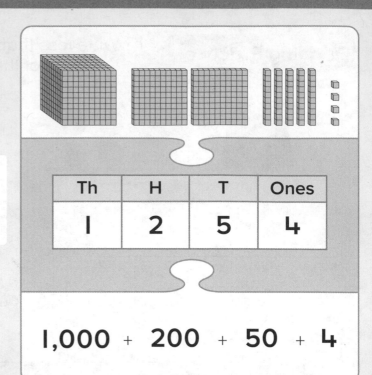

Th	H	T	Ones
1	2	5	4

1,000 + 200 + 50 + 4

What happens if you add the numbers on the bottom part?

What do you notice about the total?

How would you write this number in expanded form?

5,209

Expanded form is a way of showing how much each digit represents in a number.

Step Up

1. Look at the blocks. Write the matching number in the place-value chart. Then write the same number in expanded form.

a.
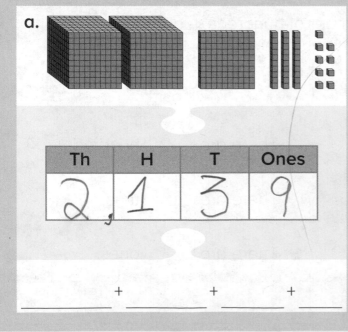

Th	H	T	Ones
2	1	3	9

____ + ____ + ____ + ____

b.
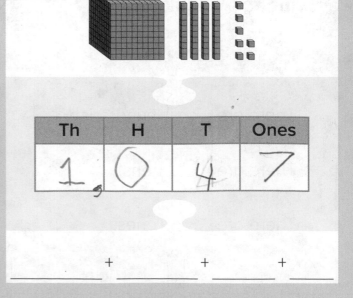

Th	H	T	Ones
1	0	4	7

____ + ____ + ____ + ____

2. Write each number in expanded form.

a.

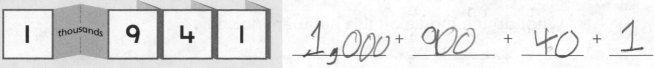

$1,000 +$ _____ 900 _____ $+ 40 + 1$

b.

$3,000 +$ _____ $900 + 90 + 0$

c.

$6,000 + 500 + 40 + 5$

d.

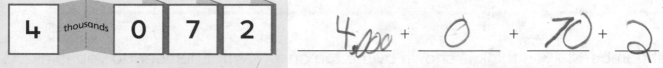

$4,000 + 0 + 70 + 2$

3. Write each number in expanded form.

a. 5,385 _____ five thousand three houjd five _____

b. 2,730 _____ two thousand siven houjd three _____

c. 8,412 _____ eaghethousand four houjd twen _____

Step Ahead Draw blocks to match the number that has been expanded. Then write the matching numeral.

$3,000 + 400 + 7$

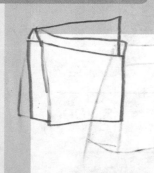
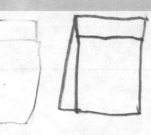
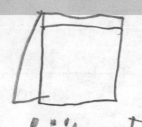

Step In What do the marks on this number line show?

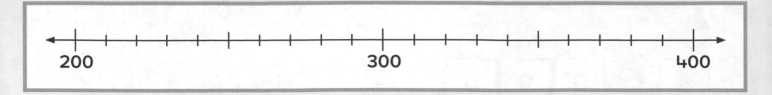

Where is 340 on the number line? Where is 295? How do you know?

What do the marks on this number line show?

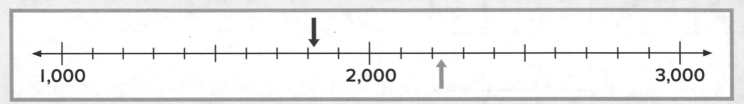

What number do you think is shown by the top arrow? What number do you think is shown by the bottom arrow? How did you figure it out?

Look at the number line below.
What numbers would you say at each mark?

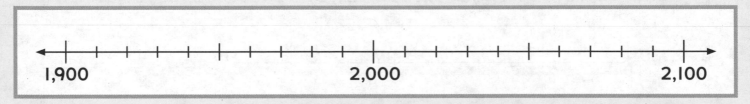

Step Up 1. Draw lines to show where the numbers belong on the number line.

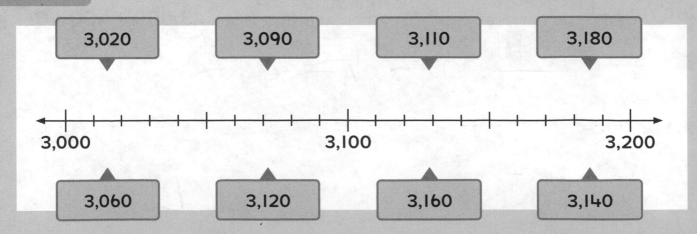

Look carefully at each of these number lines.
Then write the number that is shown by each arrow.

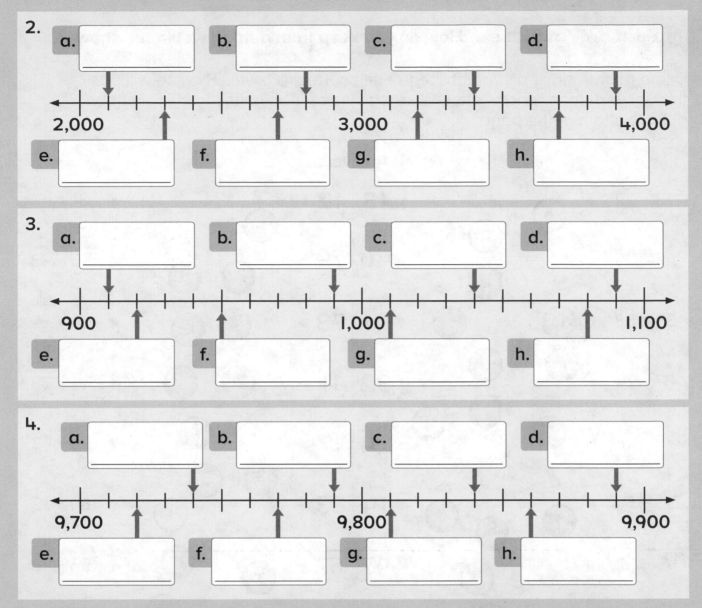

2.
a. ____ b. ____ c. ____ d. ____

2,000   3,000   4,000

e. ____ f. ____ g. ____ h. ____

3.
a. ____ b. ____ c. ____ d. ____

900   1,000   1,100

e. ____ f. ____ g. ____ h. ____

4.
a. ____ b. ____ c. ____ d. ____

9,700   9,800   9,900

e. ____ f. ____ g. ____ h. ____

Step Ahead Show the position of each number on the number line.
You can label the number line to help your thinking.

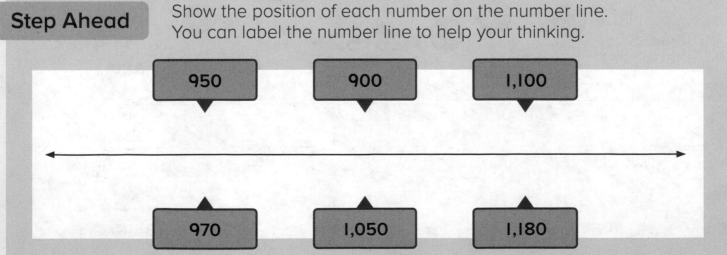

950   900   1,100

970   1,050   1,180

Computation Practice

How do you keep from getting wet in the shower?

★ Use a ruler to draw a straight line to each correct answer. The line will pass through a number and a letter. Write each letter above its matching number at the bottom of the page.

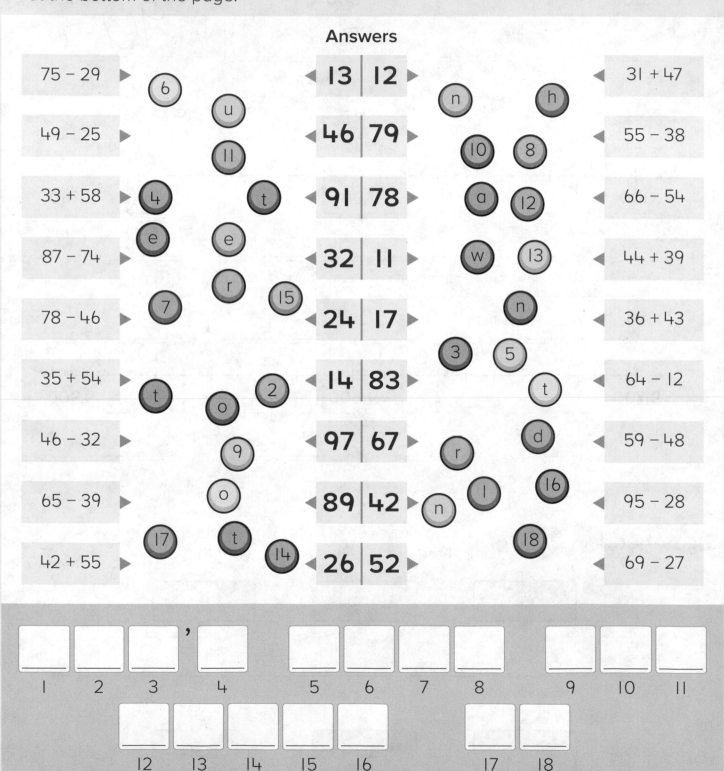

Answers

75 – 29		13 | 12		31 + 47
49 – 25		46 | 79		55 – 38
33 + 58		91 | 78		66 – 54
87 – 74		32 | 11		44 + 39
78 – 46		24 | 17		36 + 43
35 + 54		14 | 83		64 – 12
46 – 32		97 | 67		59 – 48
65 – 39		89 | 42		95 – 28
42 + 55		26 | 52		69 – 27

1   2   3   ,   4   5   6   7   8   9   10   11

12   13   14   15   16   17   18

ORIGO Stepping Stones · Grade 3 · 1.6

Ongoing Practice

I. Write **less than**, **about**, or **more than** to describe how much each container holds when compared to one liter.

Holds **exactly** I liter

a.

Holds _____
I liter

b.

Holds _____
I liter

2. Look at the blocks. Write the matching number on the place-value chart and expander.

a.

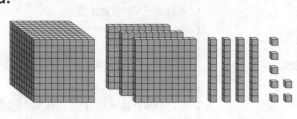

Th	H	T	Ones

thousands   hundreds

b.

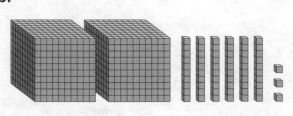

Th	H	T	Ones

thousands   hundreds

Preparing for Module 2

Draw jumps to show how you could figure out the total. Then write the total.

276 + 119 = ☐

Step In

I packed 3 stacks of boxes.
There were 8 boxes in each stack.
How many boxes did I pack?

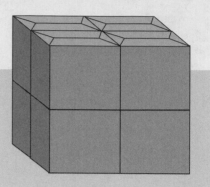

Use cubes to help figure out the answer.

Write an addition equation to match your cubes.

How does your equation relate to the story problem?

The symbol for multiplication can be used when you are adding equal groups.

Write a multiplication equation to match your cubes.

The symbol for multiplication is ×.

The result of multiplication is called the **product**.

How does your multiplication equation relate to the problem?

Step Up

1. Draw a picture to help solve each problem.
Then complete the matching multiplication sentence.

a. Each container holds 3 tennis balls. How many tennis balls will fill 4 containers?

4 containers of 3 is _____ balls

b. Kuma had 4 bags. She placed 8 oranges in each. How many oranges did she have in total?

4 bags of 8 is _____ oranges

2. Complete these. Show your thinking.

a. Balloons cost 5 cents each. How much would you pay for 9 balloons?

☐ × ☐ = ☐ cents

b. How many stamps are on a sheet that has 5 rows of 6 stamps?

☐ × ☐ = ☐ stamps

c. Each car needs 5 tires. How many tires are needed for 4 cars?

☐ × ☐ = ☐ tires

d. Henry cut 5 lengths of rope. Each piece was 4 meters long. What was the total length of the rope?

☐ × ☐ = ☐ meters

Step Ahead   **a.** Complete this table.

Number of feet	2	3	4	5	8	9	10
Number of toes							

b. How did you calculate the number of toes on 8 feet?

_____

_____

Step In Look at this sheet of stamps.

 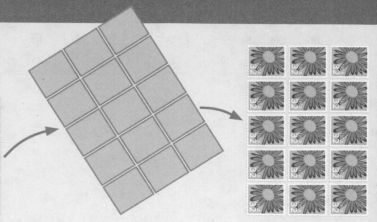

How would you describe what happened to the first array to make the second array?

What is the same about the arrays? What is different?

Write an equation to match
the first array.

☐ × ☐ = ☐

Write an equation to match
the second array.

☐ × ☐ = ☐

What is the same about the two equations? What is different?

Step Up I. Write the missing numbers to match the pictures.

a.

2 rows of 3 bananas is ☐

2 × 3 = ☐

b.

3 rows of 4 chestnuts is ☐

3 × 4 = ☐

2. Color the picture to match the story. Then complete the equation.

3 rows of 6 apples

☐ × ☐ = ☐

3. Color the picture to match the story.
Then write the matching multiplication fact and its turnaround fact.

a.   5 strawberries in each row
           4 rows of strawberries

b.   4 cherries in each row
           2 rows of cherries

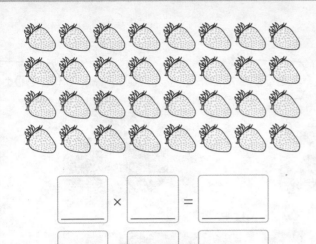

☐ × ☐ = ☐

☐ × ☐ = ☐

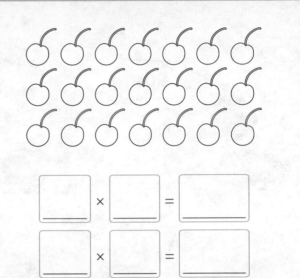

☐ × ☐ = ☐

☐ × ☐ = ☐

4. Write the turnaround fact for each equation.

a.   2 × 8 = 16

☐ × ☐ = ☐

b.   3 × 4 = 12

☐ × ☐ = ☐

c.   5 × 2 = 10

☐ × ☐ = ☐

d.   2 × 10 = 20

☐ × ☐ = ☐

e.   9 × 2 = 18

☐ × ☐ = ☐

f.   6 × 1 = 6

☐ × ☐ = ☐

Step Ahead   Write a story to match this equation.   6 × 3 = 18

Think and Solve THINK TANK Same fruits are the same price.

 90¢

 50¢

 60¢

a. = _____ ¢

b. ✱ = _____ ¢

c. = _____ ¢

Words at Work Write a multiplication word problem. Then write an equation to show the product. You can use words from the list to help.

multiply

number

how many

total

rows of

bags of

1. Draw a line from each container to the amount it holds.

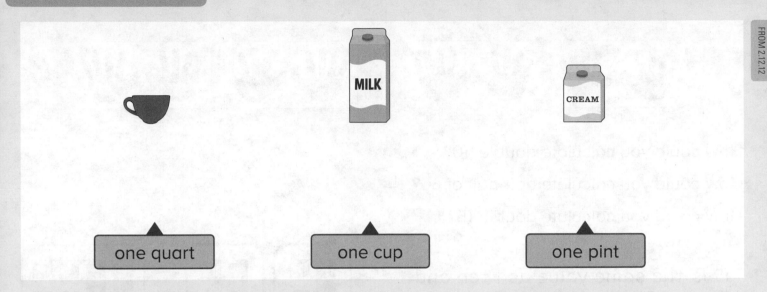

one quart   one cup   one pint

2. Write each numeral in expanded form.

a.
1,874

b.
6,310

c.
3,106

d.
4,655

Preparing for Module 2   Write each time two different ways.

a.

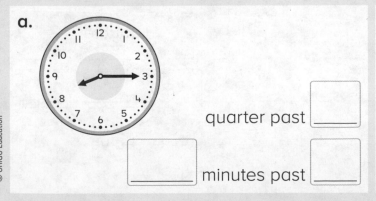

quarter past _____

_____ minutes past _____

b.

half past _____

_____ minutes past _____

FROM 2.12.12

FROM 3.1.5

Step In   What doubling or halving can you see in this picture?

How could you calculate double 40?   ~~60~~

How could you calculate one-half of 60?   30

How could you calculate double 15?   30

   15

> 15 is the same value as 1 ten and 5 ones. Double 10 is 20, double 5 is 10.

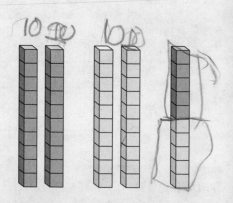

How could you calculate half of 50?   25

   50

> I think of sharing 5 tens blocks. I can put 2 tens in each group but I'd need to split the last block to share it equally.

   10 10 10

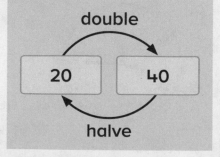

Hernando drew this picture to show what he knew about doubling and halving.

What does it tell you?

What other numbers could you use in the picture? How do you know?

double
20 → 40
halve

1. Complete these statements.

a.

double | 2 | is 4

so

double | 20 | is 40

b.

half of 6 is | 3

so

half of 60 is | 30

c.

half of 8 is | 4

so

half of 80 is | 40

d.

double | 5 | is 10

so

double | 50 | is 100

2. Complete the statement and write the answer.

a. double 15

is equal to

double | 10 | plus double | 5

so double 15 is | 30

b. double 45

is equal to

double | 20 | plus double | 5

so double 45 is | 90

c. double 35

is equal to

double | 15 | plus double | 5

so double 35 is | 70

d. double 25

is equal to

double | 10 | plus double | 5

so double 25 is | 50

Draw lines to connect the cards that have the same value.
One card has more than one match. One card has no match.

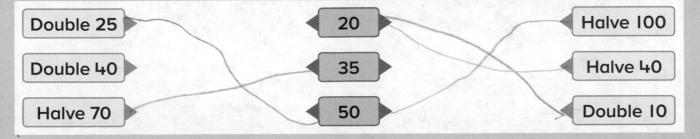

Double 25   20   Halve 100

Double 40   35   Halve 40

Halve 70   50   Double 10

Step In   Six students held up their hands in front of the class.

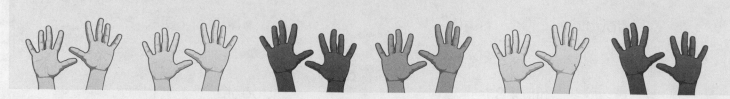

How many fingers are there in total? How can you calculate it quickly?

What multiplication equation could you write to describe the number of fingers?

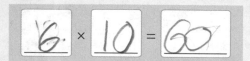

$6 \times 10 = 60$

Step Up   1.   Calculate the total. Write the matching equation.

a.

$4 \times 10 = 40$ fingers

b.

$2 \times 5 = 10$ shoes

c.

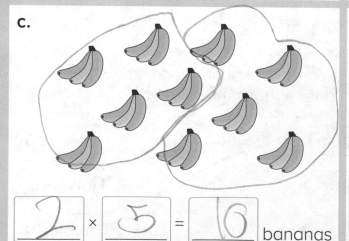

$2 \times 5 = 10$ bananas

d.

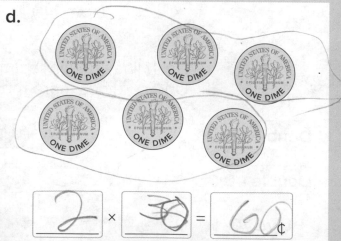

$2 \times 30 = 60$ ¢

2. Write two facts to match each array.

a.

40

| 2 | × | 20 | = | 40 |
| 4 | × | 10 | = | 40 |

b.

80

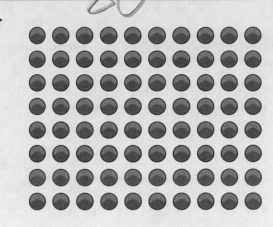

| 2 | × | 40 | = | 80 |
| 8 | × | 10 | = | |

c.

60

| 2 | × | 30 | = | 60 |
| 6 | × | 10 | = | 60 |

d.

60

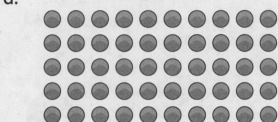

| 2 | × | 30 | = | 60 |
| 6 | × | 10 | = | 60 |

Step Ahead

Anna has 5 dimes. Marvin has 10 nickels. Does Marvin have more money than Anna? Explain your answer.

5 more ₵ caz Anna 50 ₵ ant Marvin 55 ₵.

Computation Practice   How long does it take sunlight to reach the Earth?

★ For each of these, use a ruler to draw a straight line to the correct answer. The line will pass through a letter. Write each letter in the space below its matching answer.

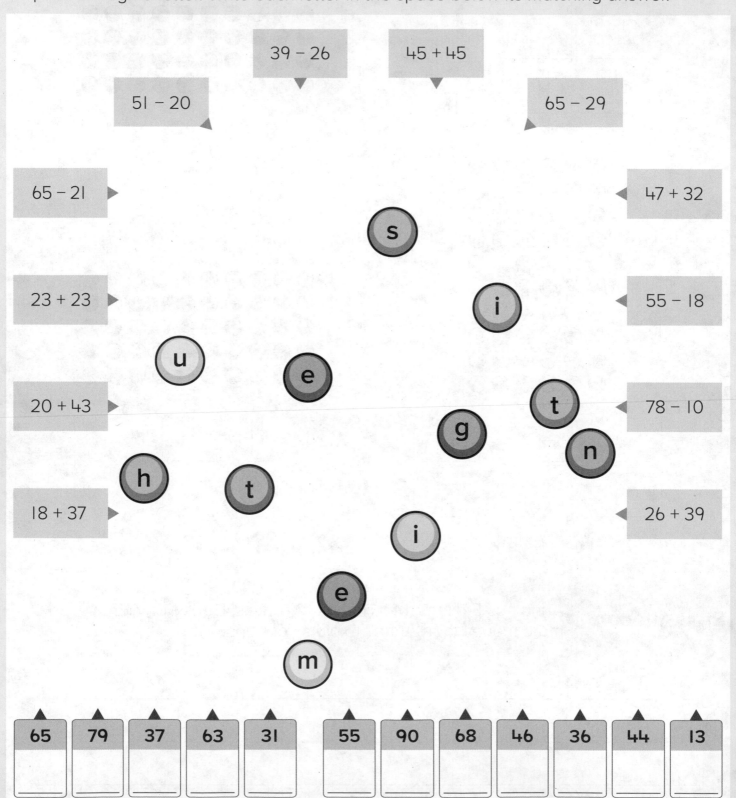

65	79	37	63	31	55	90	68	46	36	44	13

Ongoing Practice

1. Cross out blocks to help you write the number of hundreds, tens, and ones that are left. Then write the difference.

a.

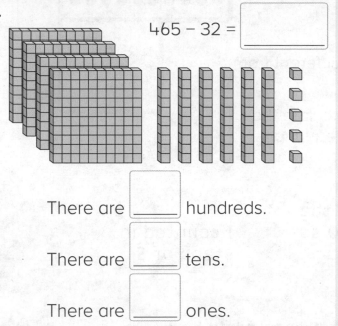

465 − 32 = _____

There are _____ hundreds.

There are _____ tens.

There are _____ ones.

b.

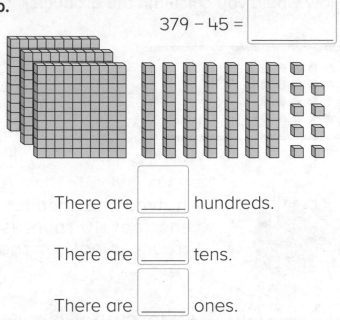

379 − 45 = _____

There are _____ hundreds.

There are _____ tens.

There are _____ ones.

2. Draw a picture to help solve each problem. Then write the matching equation.

a. Each box holds 3 golf balls.
How many golf balls are in 5 boxes?

_____ × _____ = _____ golf balls

b. Each cup holds 2 straws.
How many straws are in 4 cups?

_____ × _____ = _____ straws

Preparing for Module 2 · Write numbers to show each time.

a.

_____ minutes past _____

b.

_____ minutes past _____

Step In   Look at this array and the equations.

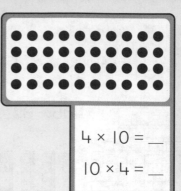

How would you calculate the products?

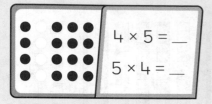

$4 \times 5 =$ __
$5 \times 4 =$ __

How is this array different from the one above?

How could you calculate the products in these equations?

$4 \times 10 =$ __
$10 \times 4 =$ __

I halved the product in the tens fact. 10 fours is 40 so 5 fours is half of that.

I counted in steps of 5.

This array shows **6 × 10**. Circle half of the array to calculate **6 × 5**.
Then complete the facts.

6 rows of 10 is ☐

so

6 rows of 5 is ☐

Step Up   1. Complete the tens fact. Circle half of the array and then complete the two fives facts to match.

a.

$3 \times 10 =$ ☐

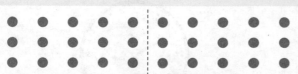

$3 \times 5 =$ ☐ $5 \times 3 =$ ☐

b.

$2 \times 10 =$ ☐

$2 \times 5 =$ ☐ $5 \times 2 =$ ☐

2. Write the product for the tens fact.
Circle half of the array and then write the two fives facts to match.

a.

$7 \times 10 =$ `70`

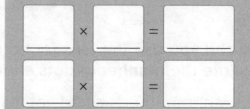

$10 \times 10 = 100$

$12 \times 12 = 124.$

b.

$6 \times 10 =$ `60`

$\underline{} \times \underline{} = \underline{}$

$\underline{} \times \underline{} = \underline{}$

c.

$9 \times 10 =$ `90`

$\underline{} \times \underline{} = \underline{}$

$\underline{} \times \underline{} = \underline{}$

d.

$8 \times 10 =$ `80`

$\underline{} \times \underline{} = \underline{}$

$\underline{} \times \underline{} = \underline{}$

Step Ahead

a. Write two tens facts to match this picture.

$\underline{} \times \underline{} = \underline{}$ $\underline{} \times \underline{} = \underline{}$

b. Cross out one hand on each card.
Then write two fives facts to match the new picture.

$\underline{} \times \underline{} = \underline{}$ $\underline{} \times \underline{} = \underline{}$

Step In

CLOSED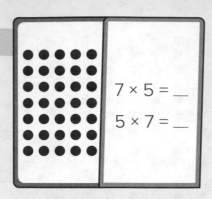

$7 \times 5 = \underline{\hspace{1cm}}$

$5 \times 7 = \underline{\hspace{1cm}}$

OPEN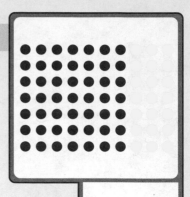

$7 \times 10 = \underline{\hspace{1cm}}$

$10 \times 7 = \underline{\hspace{1cm}}$

How can you use the tens fact on the open card to help calculate the number of dots showing on the closed card?

What other methods could you use to calculate the product of 7×5?

I would skip count by fives:
5, 10, 15, 20, 25, 30, 35.

Step Up   1.   Calculate the total and write the matching equation.

a.

5¢   5¢   5¢

5¢

5¢   5¢

$\boxed{} \times \boxed{} = \boxed{}$ ¢

b.

5¢   5¢   5¢

5¢   5¢   5¢

5¢   5¢   5¢

$\boxed{} \times \boxed{} = \boxed{}$ ¢

2. Draw nickels to match the price tag. Then write a matching equation.

a.

○ 25¢

☐ × ☐ = ☐ ¢

b.

○ 40¢

☐ × ☐ = ☐ ¢

3. Write the missing number in each equation.

a.
$6 \times 10 = $ ☐

b.
$4 \times$ ☐ $= 20$

c.
☐ $\times 5 = 35$

d.
$10 \times$ ☐ $= 40$

4. Write an equation to match each story.

a. Chloe has a set of 10 toy cars. The total length of all the cars laid end to end is 70 cm. Each car is 7 cm long.

☐ × ☐ = ☐

b. Peter had 30 stickers to pack into bags. He put 5 stickers in each bag. When he finished he had 6 bags of stickers.

☐ × ☐ = ☐

Step Ahead

These **IN** numbers are multiplied by 10 and then halved before they come **OUT**. Write the missing numbers.

IN

5

8

10

9

×10

50

☐

☐

☐

halve

OUT

25

☐

☐

☐

Think and Solve Imagine you threw three beanbags and they all landed on this target.

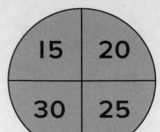

Add the numbers in your head.

a. What is the **greatest** total you can get? _____

b. What is the **least** total you can get? _____

c. Write an equation to show one way you can make a **total of 65**.

_____ + _____ + _____ = **65**

d. Write equations to show **two other ways** you can make a total of 65.

_____ + _____ + _____ = **65**   _____ + _____ + _____ = **65**

Words at Work Choose and write words from the list to complete these sentences. Some words are used more than once.

a. Nine _____ ten is ninety.

b. A multiplication _____ has a matching turnaround _____.

| equal to |
| half |
| forty |
| rows of |
| double |
| fact |

c. _____ twenty is _____.

d. _____ of eighty is _____.

e. Double thirty plus double five is _____ double thirty-five.

© ORIGO Education

Ongoing Practice

1. Cross out blocks to help you write the number of hundreds, tens, and ones that are left. Then write the difference.

a.

465 − 130 = _____

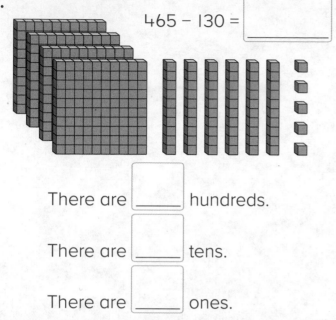

There are _____ hundreds.

There are _____ tens.

There are _____ ones.

b.

364 − 122 = _____

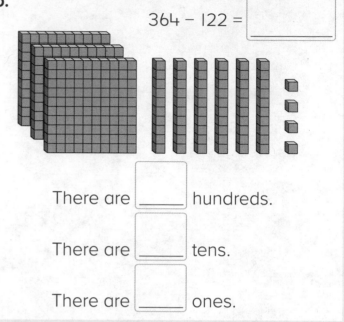

There are _____ hundreds.

There are _____ tens.

There are _____ ones.

2. Complete the statement and write the answer.

a.   **double 25**

is equal to

double _____ plus double _____

so double 25 is _____

b.   **double 35**

is equal to

double _____ plus double _____

so double 35 is _____

Preparing for Module 2

Each picture shows one corner of a **quadrilateral**. Use a ruler to complete the shapes.

a.

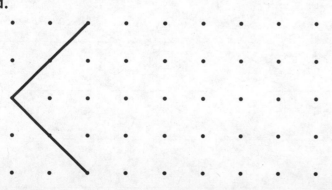

b.

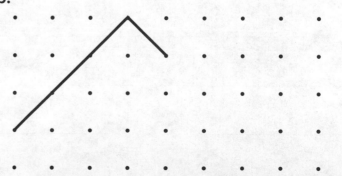

Step In   What do you know about this pan balance picture?

What equation could you write to match the picture?
What symbols must you use?

The pan balance is level so the equation must use the = symbol.

How could you use that equation to figure out these?

$26 = 15 +$ ☐ $25 = 16 +$ ☐

$27 = 15 +$ ☐ $25 = 17 +$ ☐

$28 = 15 +$ ☐ $25 = 18 +$ ☐

$29 = 15 +$ ☐ $25 = 19 +$ ☐

Which digits change in each set of equations?
Which digits stay the same?

Step Up

1. Your teacher will give you two labeled cubes. Roll the cubes and choose one number to write in **any** equation in **any** set below to make it true. Continue until all the sets have been completed.

a. SET A	b. SET B	c. SET C
$13 + \underline{} = 14$	$13 + \underline{} = 23$	$\underline{} + 6 = 66$
$13 + \underline{} = 15$	$13 + \underline{} = 33$	$50 + \underline{} = 55$
$13 + \underline{} = 16$	$13 + \underline{} = 43$	$\underline{} + 4 = 44$
$13 + \underline{} = 17$	$13 + \underline{} = 53$	$30 + \underline{} = 33$
$13 + \underline{} = 18$	$13 + \underline{} = 63$	$\underline{} + 2 = 22$
$13 + \underline{} = 19$	$13 + \underline{} = 73$	$10 + \underline{} = 11$

2. a. Look at the sets of equations in Question 1.
In Set A, how did the ones digits in the totals change?

b. In Set B, how did the tens digits in the totals change?

3. Write the missing numbers in each set below.

a.

48 + _____ = 65

49 + _____ = 65

50 + _____ = 65

51 + _____ = 65

52 + _____ = 65

b.

95 = _____ + 77

95 = _____ + 76

95 = _____ + 75

95 = _____ + 74

95 = _____ + 73

c.

13 + _____ = 105

14 + _____ = 105

15 + _____ = 105

16 + _____ = 105

17 + _____ = 105

Step Ahead

Look at how the provided answers have changed.
Complete the addition patterns.

a. **Pattern A**

The digit in the **tens** place **changes**.

_____ + 14 = 38

_____ + 14 = 48

_____ + 14 = _____

_____ + 14 = _____

_____ + 14 = _____

b. **Pattern B**

The digit in the **ones** place **changes**.

13 + 12 = _____

14 + 12 = _____

_____ + 12 = _____

_____ + 12 = _____

_____ + 12 = _____

Step In

Eva and Brady are reading the same book. Eva has read 47 pages. Brady has read 75 more pages than Eva.

How many pages has Brady read?

Do you think that Brady has read more or fewer than 100 pages?

The result of addition is called the **sum** or **total**.

How did you decide?

Lomasi uses a number line to calculate the sum.

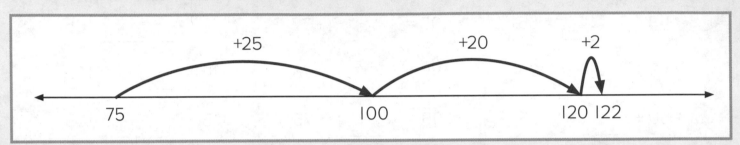

What steps does she follow?

How does she break 47 into parts to make it easier to add?

What simple pictures could you draw to figure out the sum?

47 is broken into three parts, 25 + 20 + 2. Lomasi can now jump to 100, which makes it easier to add.

Step Up

1. Draw simple pictures to show how to group the tens blocks and group the ones blocks. Then complete the sentences.

a.

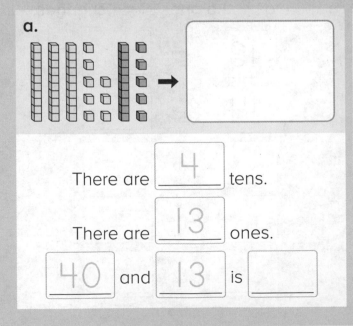

There are ☐ 4 tens.

There are ☐ 13 ones.

☐ 40 and ☐ 13 is ☐

b.

There are ☐ tens.

There are ☐ ones.

☐ and ☐ is ☐

2. Calculate each sum. Draw jumps on the number line to show your thinking.

a.

$45 + 22 = \boxed{}$

b.

$27 + 55 = \boxed{}$

c.

$85 + 29 = \boxed{}$

3. Calculate each sum. You can show your thinking on page 80.

a. $20 + 34 = \boxed{}$

b. $24 + 24 = \boxed{}$

c. $31 + 42 = \boxed{}$

d. $35 + 17 = \boxed{}$

e. $26 + 65 = \boxed{}$

f. $47 + 47 = \boxed{}$

g. $18 + 45 = \boxed{}$

h. $62 + 59 = \boxed{}$

i. $74 + 48 = \boxed{}$

Step Ahead

Britney and Kyle are collecting trading cards. Kyle has 56 cards. Britney has 20 more cards than Kyle. How many cards do they have in total?

$\boxed{}$ cards

Computation Practice

★ Use a ruler to draw a straight line to the correct total. The line will pass through a number and a letter. Write each letter above its matching number at the bottom of the page. Some totals are used more than once. Some letters appear more than once.

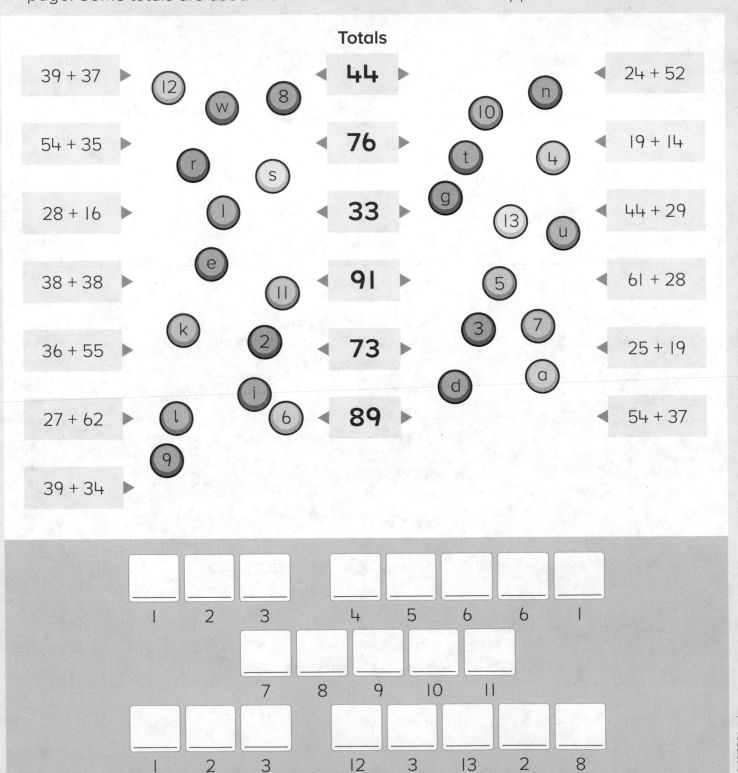

Totals

39 + 37 ▶   ◀ **44** ▶   ◀ 24 + 52

54 + 35 ▶   ◀ **76** ▶   ◀ 19 + 14

28 + 16 ▶   ◀ **33** ▶   ◀ 44 + 29

38 + 38 ▶   ◀ **91** ▶   ◀ 61 + 28

36 + 55 ▶   ◀ **73** ▶   ◀ 25 + 19

27 + 62 ▶   ◀ **89** ▶   ◀ 54 + 37

39 + 34 ▶

| 1 | 2 | 3 | | 4 | 5 | 6 | 6 | 1 |

| 7 | 8 | 9 | 10 | 11 |

| 1 | 2 | 3 | | 12 | 3 | 13 | 2 | 8 |

Ongoing Practice

1. Write the number shown by each arrow.

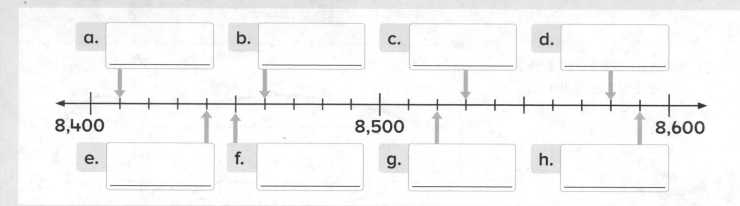

a. ____ b. ____ c. ____ d. ____

8,400   8,500   8,600

e. ____ f. ____ g. ____ h. ____

2. Complete the equations. Use a pattern to help you.

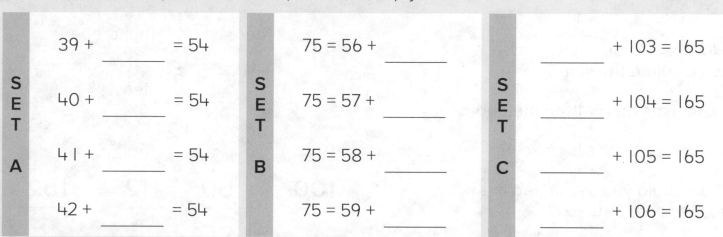

SET A

39 + _____ = 54

40 + _____ = 54

41 + _____ = 54

42 + _____ = 54

SET B

75 = 56 + _____

75 = 57 + _____

75 = 58 + _____

75 = 59 + _____

SET C

_____ + 103 = 165

_____ + 104 = 165

_____ + 105 = 165

_____ + 106 = 165

Preparing for Module 3

Write the missing numbers to describe each array.

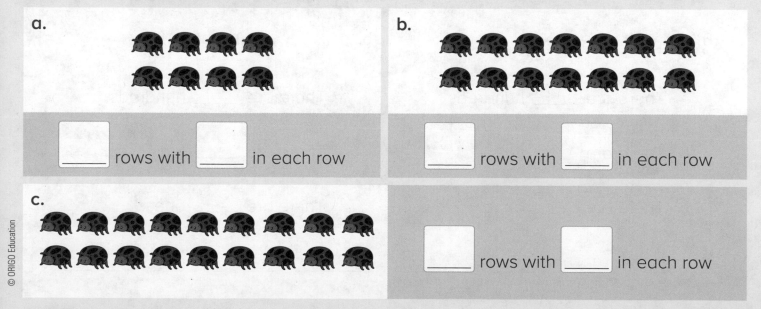

a.

_____ rows with _____ in each row

b.

_____ rows with _____ in each row

c.

_____ rows with _____ in each row

Step In

How could you calculate the total of these two prices?

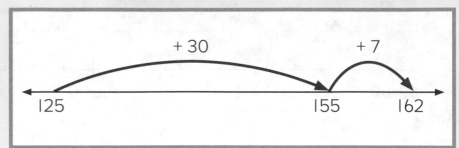

I know the total is 162 because I start with 125 then add 30 and 7 in two jumps.

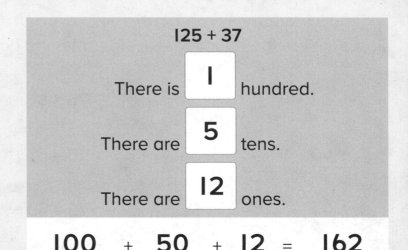

How could you use blocks to calculate the sum?

Jose uses this written method.

What steps does he follow?

How could you use Jose's method to calculate 246 + 71?

125 + 37

There is **1** hundred.

There are **5** tens.

There are **12** ones.

100 + **50** + **12** = **162**

Step Up

1. Write the number of hundreds, tens, and ones. Then write an equation to show the total. You can use blocks to help.

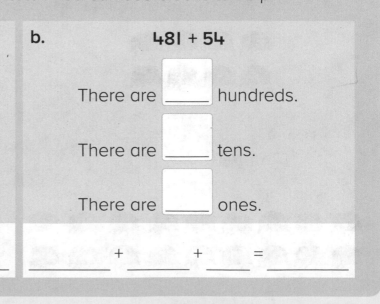

a. **324 + 63**

There are ____ hundreds.

There are ____ tens.

There are ___ ones.

____ + ____ + ____ = ____

b. **481 + 54**

There are ____ hundreds.

There are ____ tens.

There are ___ ones.

____ + ____ + ____ = ____

2. Complete these. You can use blocks to help.

a. **256 + 39**

There are ☐ hundreds.

There are ☐ tens.

There are ☐ ones.

_____ + _____ + _____ = _____

b. **684 + 41**

There are ☐ hundreds.

There are ☐ tens.

There are ☐ ones.

_____ + _____ + _____ = _____

3. Write the total. Then draw jumps on the number line to show your thinking.

a.

$316 + 48 =$ ☐

b.

$572 + 53 =$ ☐

Step Ahead Use Jose's written method to calculate each total.

a.
$214 + 49 =$ ☐

_____ + _____ + _____ = _____

b.
$762 + 84 =$ ☐

_____ + _____ + _____ = _____

Discount Air

Seattle	$135
Portland	$157
New York	$413

Step In   How would you calculate the total cost of tickets to Seattle and New York?

Do you think it is more or less than $600?
How did you form your estimate?

Carol calculates the sum like this.

What do the numbers in each row tell you?

How would you calculate the sum?

	H	T	O	
	4	1	3	
+	1	3	5	
			8	← ones total
		4	0	← tens total
	5	0	0	← hundreds total
	5	4	8	

I added the totals in each row.
That's 500 + 40 + 8.

I wrote the number of ones (8), tens (4) and hundreds (5).

Calculate the total cost of tickets to Portland and Seattle.

Step Up   1. Use Carol's strategy to calculate each sum.

a.
	H	T	O
	3	2	5
+	2	1	4

b.
	H	T	O
	5	4	1
+	2	4	7

c.
	H	T	O
	6	0	4
+	3	9	1

2. Calculate each sum.

a.

H	T	O
1	5	8
+ 1	2	4
1		2
	7	0
2	0	0
2	8	2

b.

H	T	O
3	4	8
+ 3	1	7

c.

H	T	O
6	0	9
+ 1	4	7

d.

H	T	O
2	7	6
+ 1	5	6

e.

3	9	5
+ 2	5	1

f.

4	8	6
+ 2	3	2

g.

7	4	0
+ 1	9	8

h.

3	8	5
+ 1	7	6

Step Ahead

Deana attended a training course. Her flights cost $216 and her overnight stay was $135. The course fees were $130. How much did she spend in total? Show your thinking.

$ _____

Think and Solve

For each square, add the numbers in the shaded boxes to figure out the **magic number**.

Complete each magic square.

a.
16		14
12	17	10

b.
6	11	
	7	9
10	3	

> In a magic square, the three numbers in each row, column, and diagonal add to make the same number. This is called the **magic number**.

Words at Work

Write in words how you can solve this equation on a number line. You can use words from the list and draw a diagram to help.

216 + 38 = ?

| jump |
| total |
| hundreds |
| tens |
| ones |
| add |
| sum |

I. Write the matching number on the expander and in words.

FROM 3.1.4

a. 3,605

thousands

b. 7,091

thousands

2. Write the number of hundreds, tens, and ones. Then write an equation to show the total. You can use blocks to help.

FROM 3.2.3

a.   **267 + 25**

There are _____ hundreds.

There are _____ tens.

There are _____ ones.

_____ + _____ + _____ = _____

b.   **354 + 72**

There are _____ hundreds.

There are _____ tens.

There are _____ ones.

_____ + _____ + _____ = _____

Preparing for Module 3   Double the tens, **then** double the ones. Write the total.

a. 24 + 24

Double 20 is 40

Double _____ is _____

40 + _____ = _____

b. 32 + 32

Double _____ is _____

Double _____ is _____

_____ + _____ = _____

Step In

The table shows the passing yards that were made by the same quarterback over four games.

How could you calculate the total passing yards for Games 1 and 2?

PASSING YARDS

Game 1	224 yards
Game 2	307 yards
Game 3	181 yards
Game 4	235 yards

I can figure that out in my head. It is 300 + 224 + 7.

How could you calculate the total passing yards for Games 3 and 4?

These two numbers are harder to add so I'll record my steps.

H	T	O
2	3	5
+ 1	8	1
		6
1	1	0
3	0	0
4	1	6

What is your estimate of the total passing yards that were made over all four games?

Step Up

1. Use a mental or written method to calculate the total passing yards for each of these.

PASSING YARDS

Game 1	153 yards
Game 2	235 yards
Game 3	319 yards
Game 4	290 yards

a. Games 1 and 2

_____ yards

b. Games 3 and 4

_____ yards

2. Solve each problem. Show your thinking.

a. 199 hotdogs were sold in the first half and 175 hotdogs in the second half. How many hotdogs were sold?

_____ hotdogs

b. 246 people went to Game 1. 60 more went to Game 2 than Game 1. How many people went to the two games?

_____ people

c. The team travels 142 miles to the first match, 139 miles to the next match, and 105 miles home. What is the total distance traveled?

_____ miles

d. 189 tickets are sold in one hour. This is 105 fewer than in the next hour. How many were sold in the next hour?

_____ tickets

Step Ahead Each table shows the running yards that were made by three players. Circle the players who ran 300 yards or more.

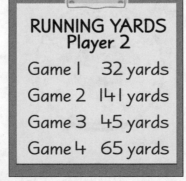

RUNNING YARDS Player 1	
Game 1	92 yards
Game 2	47 yards
Game 3	75 yards
Game 4	97 yards

RUNNING YARDS Player 2	
Game 1	32 yards
Game 2	141 yards
Game 3	45 yards
Game 4	65 yards

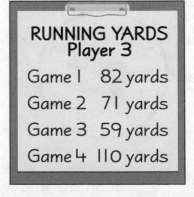

RUNNING YARDS Player 3	
Game 1	82 yards
Game 2	71 yards
Game 3	59 yards
Game 4	110 yards

Step In

**What time is shown on this clock?
How do you know?**

20 minutes past 7.

I could also say seven twenty.

What do you notice about the minute hand on this clock?

What do the marks between the numbers on the clock tell you?

How many minutes past the hour is the clock showing?

What time is shown on the clock?

Write numbers on the digital clock to show the same time.

What do the numbers on the left side of the colon tell you?

What do the numbers on the right side of the colon tell you?

If this time is before noon, would you write a.m. or p.m. after the time?

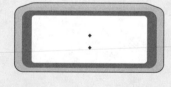

Step Up

1. Write the number of minutes past each hour.

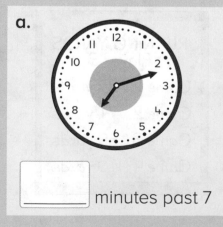

a.

_____ minutes past 7

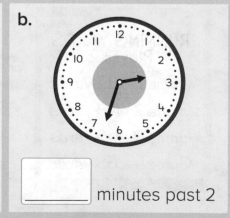

b.

_____ minutes past 2

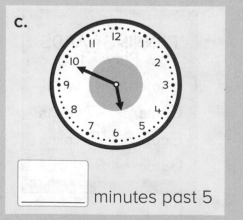

c.

_____ minutes past 5

2. Write each time.

a.

____ minutes past ____

b.

____ minutes past ____

c.

____ minutes past ____

d.

____ minutes past ____

e.

____ minutes past ____

f.

____ minutes past ____

3. Draw hands on the clock to match the time.

a.
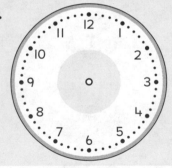

23 minutes past 9

b.

45 minutes past 3

c.

4 minutes past 7

Step Ahead Henry needs to heat a piece of pie for 10 minutes.

This clock shows the time that he put the pie in the oven.
At what time should he take the pie out?

_____

Computation Practice

Which hand should you use to stir coffee?

★ Complete the equations. Then write each letter above its matching difference at the bottom of the page. Some letters appear more than once.

95 − 18 = ___	**y**	55 − 29 = ___	**h**
75 − 19 = ___	**n**	85 − 28 = ___	**a**
55 − 28 = ___	**e**	95 − 49 = ___	**u**
85 − 69 = ___	**t**	85 − 38 = ___	**d**
55 − 38 = ___	**l**	75 − 39 = ___	**p**
95 − 19 = ___	**i**	95 − 58 = ___	**r**
95 − 28 = ___	**s**	85 − 19 = ___	**o**

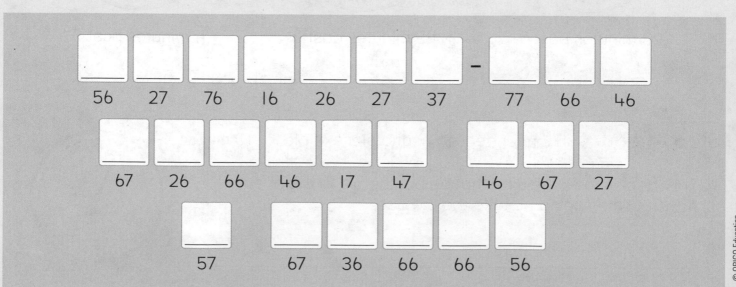

							-		
56	27	76	16	26	27	37	77	66	46

67	26	66	46	17	47	46	67	27

57	67	36	66	66	56

1. Draw coins to pay the exact amount for each stamp.

a.

USA
36¢

b.

USA
95¢

2. Solve each problem. Show your thinking.

a. A family drove 57 miles to a theme park. The entry price was $228 and they spent $65 on lunch. How much money did they spend at the theme park?

$_____

b. Terek earns $27 and adds it to his savings. He now has $193 in savings. How much money did he have in savings before?

$_____

Preparing for Module 3

Use a double you know to figure out these doubles. Write the numbers to show your thinking.

a.　　Double 6

Double | 5 | is _____

Double | 1 | is _____

(SO)

Double | 6 | is _____

b.　　Double 8

Double | ☐ | is _____

Double | ☐ | is _____

(SO)

Double | 8 | is _____

c.　　Double 7

Double | ☐ | is _____

Double | ☐ | is _____

(SO)

Double | 7 | is _____

Step In

How can you figure out the number of minutes past the hour shown on this clock?

How do you read the time past the hour?

How can you figure out the number of minutes to the next hour?

Write numbers to complete these two ways of reading this time.

 minutes past o'clock

 minutes to o'clock

How many minutes past the hour does this digital clock show?

How can you figure out the number of minutes to the next hour?

5:42

Is there another way you could figure it out?

Complete these to show two ways of reading the digital time above.

 minutes past o'clock

 minutes to o'clock

Step Up

1. Write the number of minutes past the hour and the number of minutes to the next hour. Then write the time on the digital clock.

a.

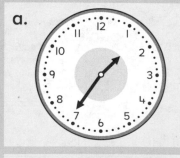

_____ minutes past _____

_____ minutes to _____

b.

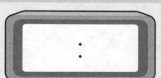

_____ minutes past _____

 minutes to

2. Complete these to show matching times.

a.

_____ minutes past _____

_____ minutes to _____

[:]

b.

_____ minutes past _____

_____ minutes to _____

[:]

c.

_____ minutes past _____

_____ minutes to _____

[:]

3. Complete these.

a.

`6:58` _____ minutes to _____

b.

`2:45` _____ minutes to _____

c.

`10:36` _____ minutes to _____

d.

`5:48` _____ minutes to _____

Step Ahead Circle the times that **you** could easily read as minutes to the hour.

`4:45`   `11:03`

© ORIGO Education

Step In

Think about all the different ways you could read this time.

45 minutes after 2.

15 minutes before 3.

Two forty-five.

A quarter to 3.

What other ways do you know?

What are all the different ways you could read these times?

Step Up

1. Write three different ways you could say each time.

a.

b.

© ORIGO Education

2. Draw lines to connect times to the correct clock.
Cross out the time that does not have a match.

a.

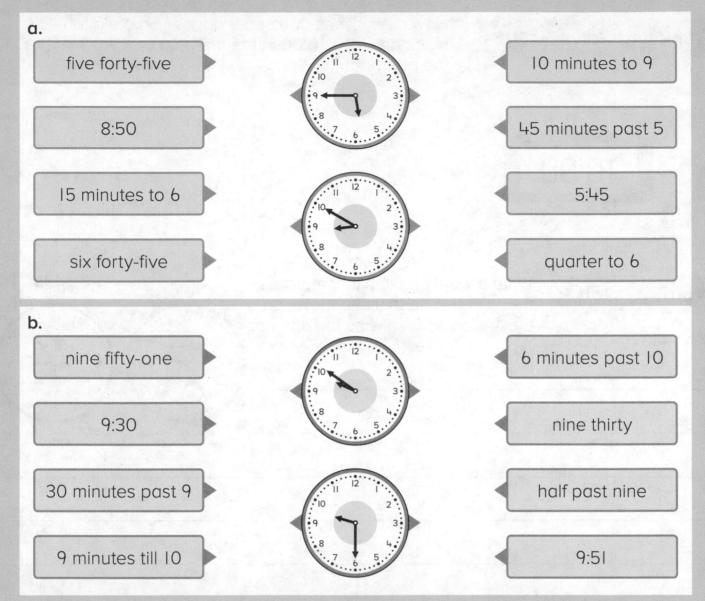

five forty-five		10 minutes to 9
8:50		45 minutes past 5
15 minutes to 6		5:45
six forty-five		quarter to 6

b.

nine fifty-one		6 minutes past 10
9:30		nine thirty
30 minutes past 9		half past nine
9 minutes till 10		9:51

Step Ahead   Use the clock to help you solve the word problem.

Three friends arrive at school at different times.
Emma arrives at seven fifty. Jack is dropped off
at a quarter to eight. Abigail gets there at eight fifteen.

Write the names of the three friends in order from who
arrives at school first to who arrives last.

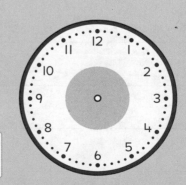

first	second	third

© ORIGO Education

Think and Solve  How many times does an 8 appear on a digital clock between 10:00 in the morning and 2:00 in the afternoon?

10:00

Words at Work

Write a word problem that matches the start and finish times shown on these clocks. Then write the answer.

start

finish

Ongoing Practice

I. Draw bills and coins to match each amount.

$	¢

a. six dollars and seventy-two cents

b. ten dollars and sixty-seven cents

2. Write each time.

a.

_____ minutes past _____

b.

_____ minutes past _____

c.

_____ minutes past _____

Preparing for Module 3

Write **is greater than** or **is less than** to make each statement true.

a.

573 | _____ | 734

b.

989 | _____ | 998

c.

291 | _____ | 219

Step In

Akari rides the school bus home each day. The school bus departs at 3:25 p.m. Akari is dropped off in front of her house at 4:05 p.m.

How could you figure out the length of Akari's bus trip home each day?

Cole uses a number line to figure out the length of the trip.

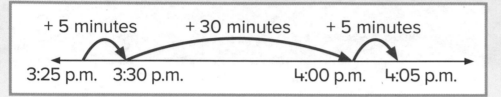

+ 5 minutes   + 30 minutes   + 5 minutes

3:25 p.m.   3:30 p.m.   4:00 p.m.   4:05 p.m.

What steps does Cole follow?

How long is the bus trip?

Making jumps to a time that is on the hour or half-past the hour can be helpful.

Step Up

1. These clocks all show times after noon on the same day. Calculate the length of each trip.

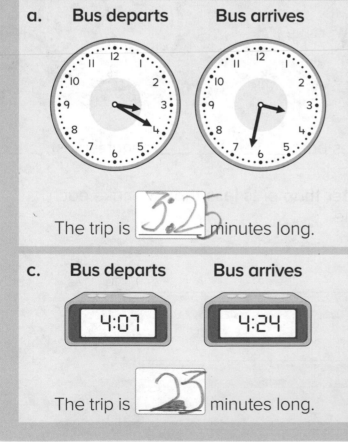

a. **Bus departs**   **Bus arrives**

The trip is ⟨3:25⟩ minutes long.

c. **Bus departs**   **Bus arrives**

4:07   4:24

The trip is ⟨23⟩ minutes long.

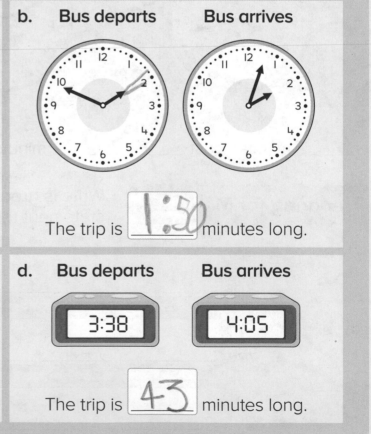

b. **Bus departs**   **Bus arrives**

The trip is ⟨1:50⟩ minutes long.

d. **Bus departs**   **Bus arrives**

3:38   4:05

The trip is ⟨43⟩ minutes long.

2. Draw jumps on the number line to solve each problem.

a. Carrina answers the phone at 7:45 a.m. She ends the call at 8:10 a.m. How long was the phone call?

25 minutes

+15   +20

b. A frozen pizza is put in the oven at 1:35 p.m. The pizza is taken out of the oven 40 minutes later. At what time was the pizza taken out?

2.15 p.m.

+ 20   +20

c. A game starts at 2:52 p.m. and goes for 21 minutes. When did the game finish?

3:03 p.m.

d. A movie starts 6:35 p.m. and ends at 8:15 p.m. How long is the movie?

2h20 minutes

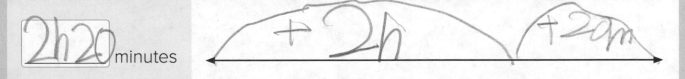
+ 2h   +20m

Step Ahead   Use the clock to help you solve each problem.

a. The train departs at 7:14 a.m. and arrives at Central Station 8 minutes later. At what time does it arrive?

7:22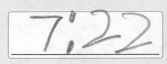

b. It takes Luis 15 minutes to ride to school. If he arrives at 8:04 a.m., at what time did he leave?

8:19

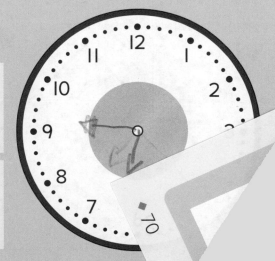

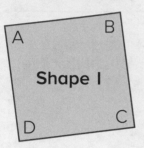

Step In   **What do you notice about these quadrilaterals?**

Compare the corners of each shape. What do you notice?

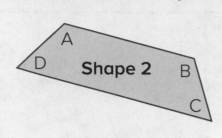

Shape 1

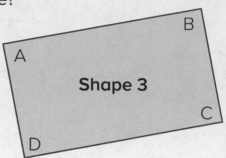

Shape 2

Shape 3

What is different about the corners of Shape 2?

What type of rectangle is Shape 1?
What type of rectangle is Shape 3?

Quadrilaterals that have all corners the same size are called **rectangles**.

For Shape 1 and Shape 3, all the corners look the same size.

Step Up   I. Each picture shows one corner of a quadrilateral. Draw the other two sides to make a square or non-square rectangle.

a.

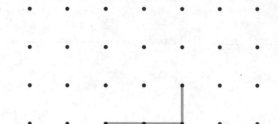

b.

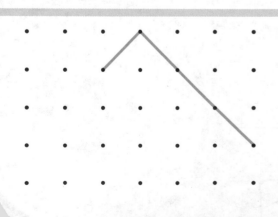

c.

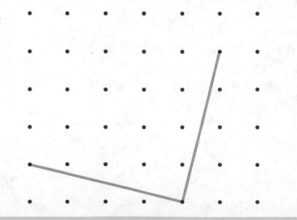

d.

2. Draw lines between dots to split each shape into **three** rectangles. The first one has been done for you.

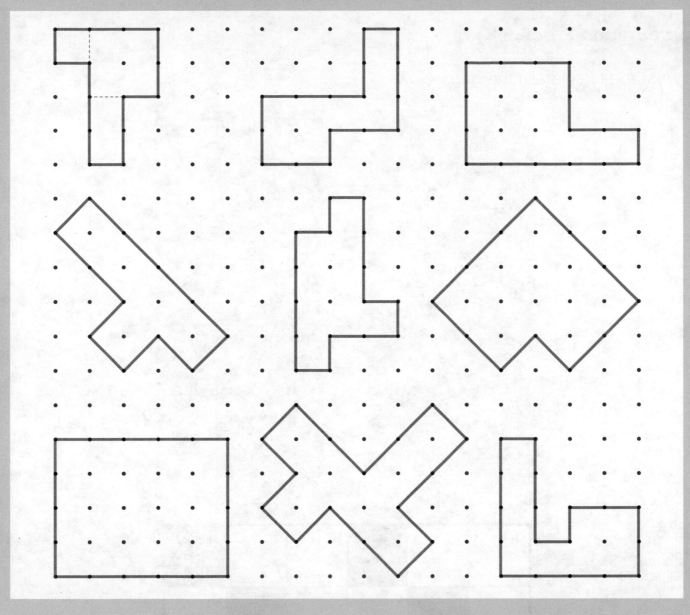

Step Ahead Shapes can be joined together to make other shapes. For example, these two triangles make a square.

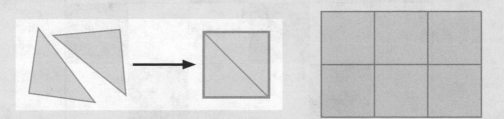

How many rectangles are in the picture on the right? Remember, shapes can be joined together. Look for rectangles of different sizes and shapes. _____

Computation Practice

★ Write the answers in the grid below.

Across	Down
a. 85 − 48	**a.** 23 + 16
b. 33 + 29	**b.** 95 − 29
c. 20 + 46	**c.** 88 − 23
e. 57 − 22	**d.** 44 − 10
f. 39 + 25	**e.** 15 + 15
g. 45 + 45	**f.** 96 − 32
h. 76 − 62	**g.** 62 + 37
i. 10 + 37	**h.** 75 − 58
k. 67 − 57	**i.** 20 + 20
l. 65 − 29	**j.** 23 + 23

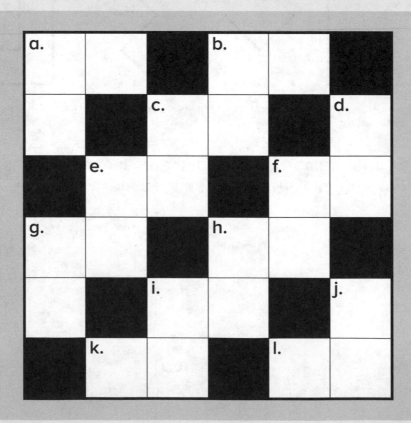

Ongoing Practice

1. Look at this graph.

Favorite Fruit Juice   ⏣ means 1 vote

Apple	⏣	⏣	⏣	⏣	⏣		
Orange	⏣	⏣	⏣	⏣	⏣	⏣	⏣
Grape	⏣	⏣					

a. Which juice is the most popular? _____

b. How many people like Apple juice? _____

c. What is the difference between the number of votes for Orange and the number of votes for Grape? _____

2. Complete these to show matching times.

a. _____ minutes past _____

_____ minutes to _____

_____ minutes past _____

_____ minutes to _____

b.

Preparing for Module 3

This table shows money raised for charity.

	Week				
	One	Two	Three	Four	Five
	$49	$45	$78	$57	$62

a. Write the amounts that are **greater than** $50.

b. Write the amounts in order from **greatest** to **least**.

_____ , _____ , _____ , _____ , _____

2D shapes: Exploring rhombuses

Step In   Circle each shape that has all sides of equal length.

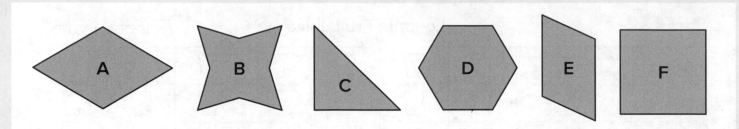

Which shapes are quadrilaterals?

The word **rhombus** is used to describe quadrilaterals that have four sides of equal length. Which shapes above are rhombuses?

Step Up   1.   Circle each rhombus. Use a centimeter ruler to help you decide.

a.
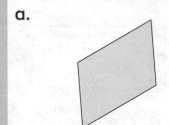

b.

c.

d.
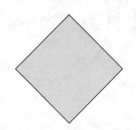

e.
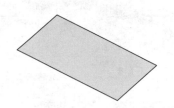

f.
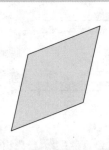

g.
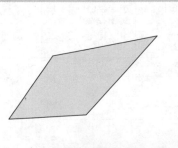

h.
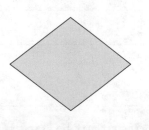

i.

2.   Write **R** inside the shapes in Question 1 that are rectangles.

3. Donna wants to make rhombuses with groups of straws. She must use **all** the straws in each group. Count and measure the straws in each group below and color the ⬭ beside the correct answer.

a.

⬭ Can make a rhombus.
⬭ Can't make a rhombus.

b.

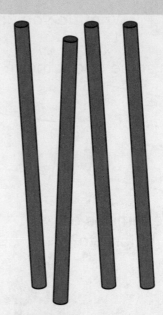

⬭ Can make a rhombus.
⬭ Can't make a rhombus.

c.

⬭ Can make a rhombus.
⬭ Can't make a rhombus.

d.

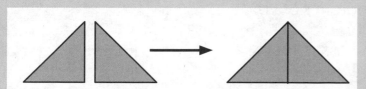

⬭ Can make a rhombus.
⬭ Can't make a rhombus.

e.

⬭ Can make a rhombus.
⬭ Can't make a rhombus.

Step Ahead

Shapes can be joined together to make larger shapes. For example, these two triangles can be joined to make a larger triangle.

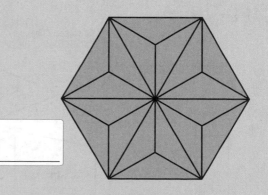

How many rhombuses are in the picture on the right? _____

Remember shapes can be joined together.
Look for rhombuses of different sizes.

Step In

What do you know about these shapes?

What is the same about them? What is different?

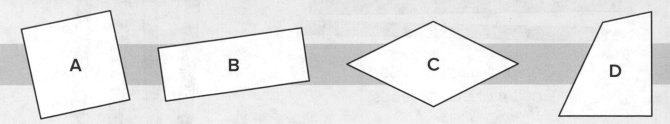

What shape families do the shapes belong to?

> Shape A is a quadrilateral because it has 4 straight sides. It is also a square, which is a type of rhombus because all its sides are equal. It is also a type of rectangle because all its corners are the same size.

This tree diagram shows how quadrilaterals are related.

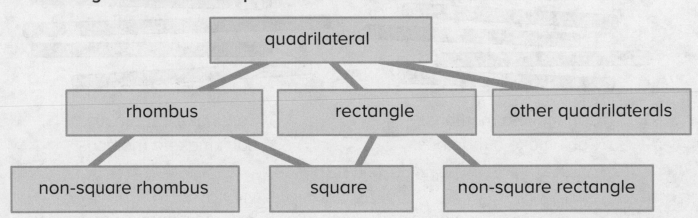

Step Up

1. Look at the shapes below. Circle those shapes that do **not** belong anywhere in the tree diagram above.

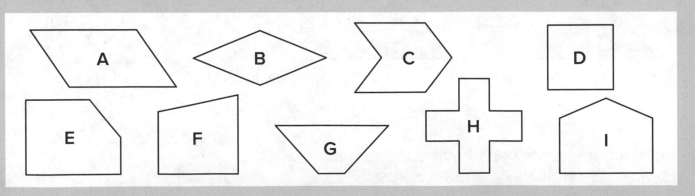

2. Cut out the shapes from the support page and paste them in the correct spaces below. Some shapes do not belong in any of the spaces. These will be used in the next question.

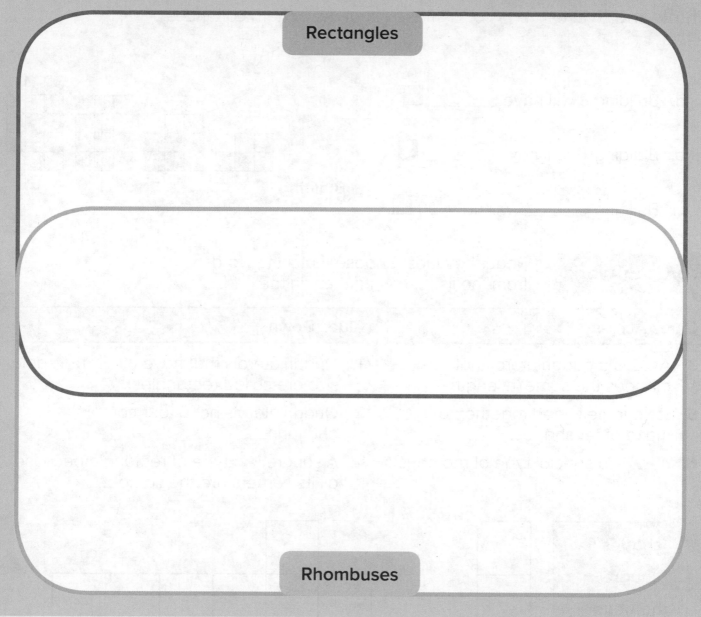

Rectangles

Rhombuses

Step Ahead

Look at the shapes from the support page that do not belong in the diagram above. Paste them below, then draw one other shape that also does not belong.

Think and Solve Imagine that the pattern continues.

a. Building 8 will have _____ ▪.

b. Building 11 will have _____ ▪.

c. Building _____ will have 29 ▪.

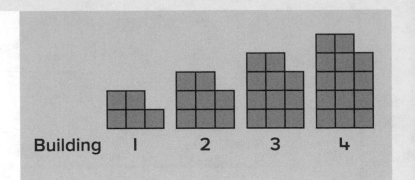

Building   1   2   3   4

Words at Work
Read the clues. Choose matching words from the list and write them in the grid.

Clues Across

3. A ___ is a quadrilateral that has all sides the same in length.

5. ___ can be joined together to make other shapes.

6. A ___ is a special type of rhombus.

Clues Down

1. Quadrilaterals that have all ___ the same size are called rectangles.

2. Quadrilaterals have four corners and four ___.

4. A square is a type of rectangle because all its corners are the same ___.

shapes

square

rhombus

size

sides

corners

Ongoing Practice

1. Look at this graph.

Favorite Season

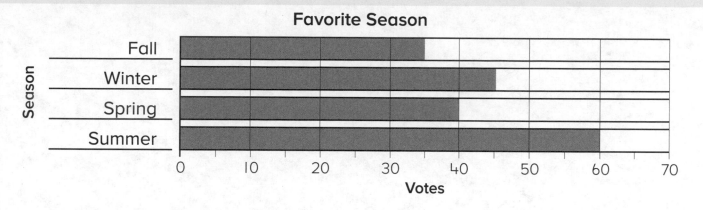

a. What are the two most popular seasons? _____ and _____

b. How many more votes did Winter get than Fall? _____

c. What is the difference in votes between Summer and Fall? _____

2. Read the analog clock. Then write the same time on the digital clock.

a.

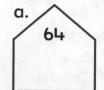

b.

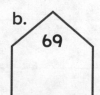

c.

Preparing for Module 3

For each number, write the **ten** that is closest. Think about a number line to help.

a.
64
_____

b.
69
_____

c.
73
_____

d.
76
_____

e.
71
_____

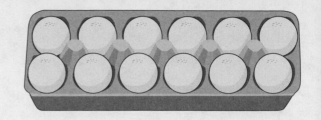

Step In

What do you see in this picture?

What doubles fact is shown in the picture?

What equation could you write to match the picture of eggs?

What do you see in this picture?

Write a multiplication fact and its turnaround fact to match.

	×		=	

	×		=	

How did you figure out the product?

What are some other problems you could solve by doubling?

I have used doubling with addition.

Step Up   I.   Write a twos multiplication fact and its turnaround for each picture.

a.	b.	c.

a.

_____ × _____ = _____

_____ × _____ = _____

b.

_____ × _____ = _____

_____ × _____ = _____

c.

_____ × _____ = _____

_____ × _____ = _____

2. Write the twos fact that matches each array. Then write the turnaround fact.

a.

_____ × _____ = _____

_____ × _____ = _____

b.

_____ × _____ = _____

_____ × _____ = _____

c.

_____ × _____ = _____

_____ × _____ = _____

3. Draw a line to match each equation with its turnaround below.
Then complete the equations.

2 × 9 = _____

12 × 2 = _____

11 × 2 = _____

2 × 14 = _____

2 × 12 = _____

2 × 11 = _____

9 × 2 = _____

14 × 2 = _____

Step Ahead   Write the missing numbers.

a.
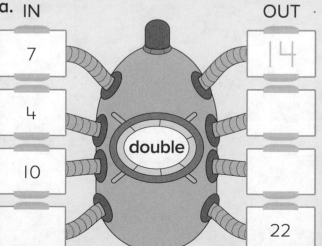

b.
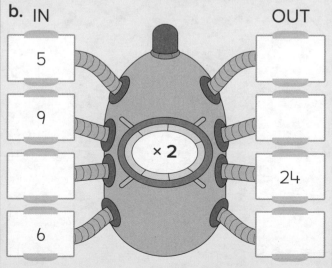

Step In What pictures could you draw to match this fact? $2 \times 7 = 14$

Wendell drew rows of apples.
How does his picture match the fact?

becus It like 7+7 but insteb Its times so now 14 2×7

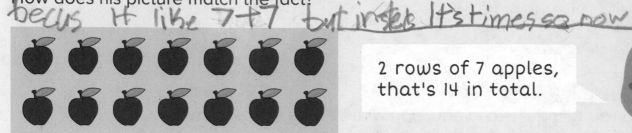

2 rows of 7 apples,
that's 14 in total.

Isabelle drew bags of marbles.

How does her picture match the fact?

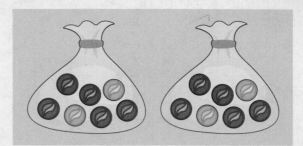

How could you represent the same fact on a number line?

You could draw 2 jumps of 7 on a number line.

Step Up 1. Draw a picture to match each equation.

a. $5 \times 2 = 10$

b. $3 \times 2 = 6$

2. Complete the equation.
Then draw jumps on the number line to show your thinking.

a.

$2 \times 6 = 12$

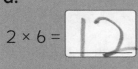

b. Jumps of

$4 \times 2 = 8$

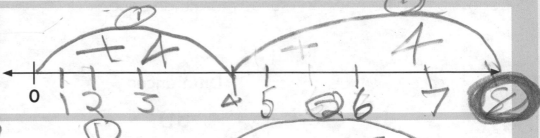

c. Jumps of

$2 \times 5 = 10$

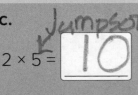

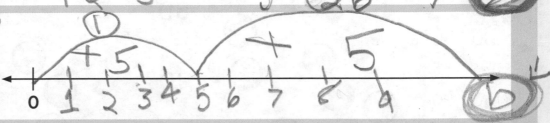

d. Jumps of

$9 \times 2 = 18$

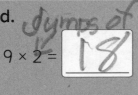

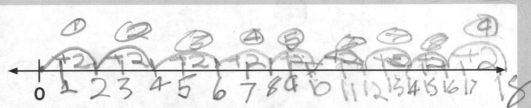

3. Write the missing number in each equation.

a. $8 \times 2 = \boxed{}$

b. $\boxed{} \times 2 = 10$

c. $10 \times \boxed{} = 20$

d. $\boxed{} \times 3 = 6$

e. $2 \times \boxed{} = 20$

f. $14 = \boxed{} \times 2$

g. $2 \times \boxed{} = 8$

h. $12 = 6 \times \boxed{}$

Step Ahead   Write a multiplication equation you could use to solve each problem.

a. There are 9 boxes of shoes.
Each box holds 2 shoes.
How many shoes in total?

$\boxed{} \times \boxed{} = \boxed{}$

b. Luke cuts 14 meters of rope into
lengths of 2 meters. How many
lengths can he cut?

$\boxed{} \times \boxed{} = \boxed{}$

Computation Practice How do you make a skeleton laugh?

★ Use a ruler to draw a straight line to the correct difference. The line will pass through a letter and a number. Write the letter above its matching number at the bottom of the page. Some differences are used more than once.

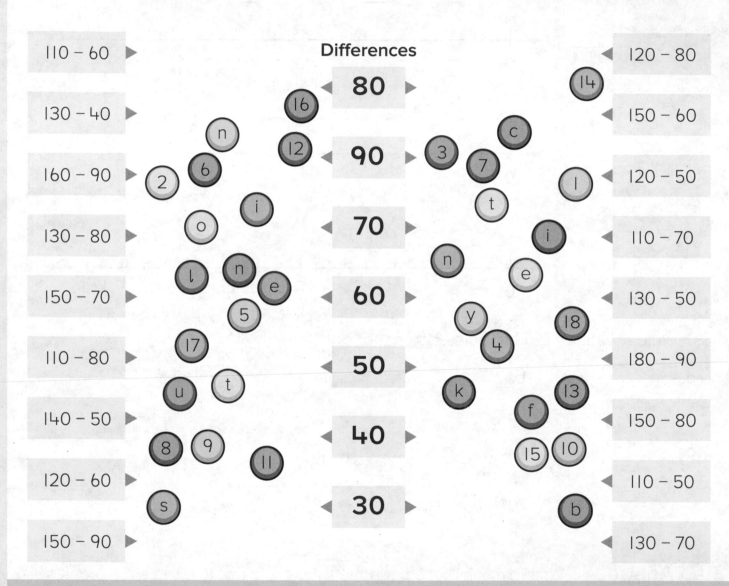

110 – 60 ▶   **Differences**   ◀ 120 – 80

130 – 40 ▶   **80**   ◀ 150 – 60

160 – 90 ▶   **90**   ◀ 120 – 50

130 – 80 ▶   **70**   ◀ 110 – 70

150 – 70 ▶   **60**   ◀ 130 – 50

110 – 80 ▶   **50**   ◀ 180 – 90

140 – 50 ▶   **40**   ◀ 150 – 80

120 – 60 ▶   ◀ 110 – 50

   30

150 – 90 ▶   ◀ 130 – 70

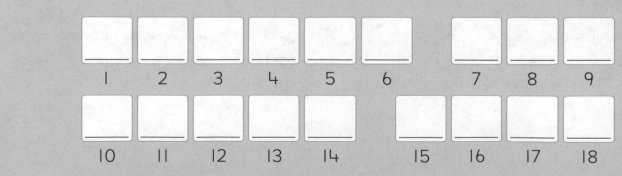

1 2 3 4 5 6   7 8 9

10 11 12 13 14   15 16 17 18

1. Color one part of each strip red. Then circle the strip that shows **one-fourth** red.

FROM 2.12.4

2. Write a twos multiplication fact and its turnaround to match each picture.

FROM 3.3.1

a.

_____ × _____ = _____

_____ × _____ = _____

b.

_____ × _____ = _____

_____ × _____ = _____

c.

_____ × _____ = _____

_____ × _____ = _____

Preparing for Module 4   Write the number in each group.

a.

9 books   **3** backpacks

_____ books in each backpack

b.

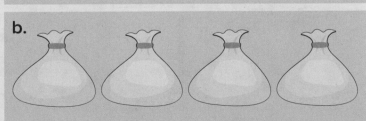

12 marbles   **4** bags

_____ marbles in each bag

Step In

Complete each sentence to match this picture of blocks.

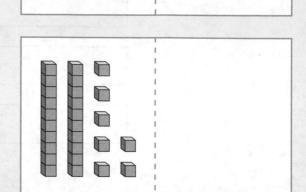

Double 13 = ☐

2 × 13 = ☐

Draw more blocks to show double 27.

How would you calculate the total?

Double the number of tens. Then double the number of ones. Double 20 is 40. Double 7 is 14. 40 plus 14 is 54.

What strategy could you use to calculate 2 × 48?

Step Up

1. Draw more blocks to double each number. Then complete the equations.

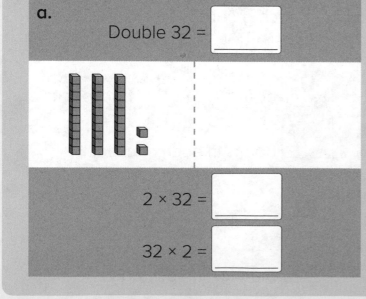

a.

Double 32 = ☐

2 × 32 = ☐

32 × 2 = ☐

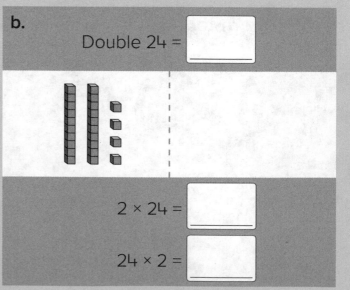

b.

Double 24 = ☐

2 × 24 = ☐

24 × 2 = ☐

2. Complete the equations. You can draw blocks to help your thinking.

a.
Double 38 = [ ]

2 × 38 = [ ]

38 × 2 = [ ]

b.
Double 29 = [ ]

2 × 29 = [ ]

29 × 2 = [ ]

3. Complete each equation. Show your thinking.

a.
2 × 35 = [ ]

b.
47 × 2 = [ ]

Step Ahead   Write the missing numbers.

a.
2 × [ ] = 90

b.
[ ] × 2 = 52

Step In   There are six jelly beans in each bag.

How can you figure out the total number of jelly beans without counting each one?

Think **double double** to multiply by 4.

Double 6 is 12.
Double 12 is 24.
So, 4 × 6 = 24.

Use the same thinking to figure out how many cookies are on this tray.

Complete this sentence to match.

Double 8 is ___16___, double ___25___ is ___50___.

What other numbers could you multiply by 4 using this strategy?

Step Up   I.   Use the **double-double strategy** to complete the equation.

a.

Double | Double

4 × 3 = __12__

double 3 is __6__

double __4__ is __8__

b.

Double | Double

4 × 7 = __28__

double 7 is __14__

double __14__ is __28__

2. Use the **double-double strategy** to complete the equation.
Then write the turnaround fact.

a.

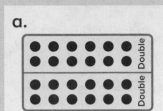

$4 \times 6 = 24$

$6 \times 4 = 36$

double 6 is **12**

double 12 is 24

b.

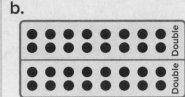

$4 \times 8 = 36$

$8 \times 4 = 24$

double 5 is 10

double 10 is 20

c.

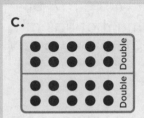

$4 \times 5 = 20$

$5 \times 4 = 19$

double 20 is 40

double 40 is 80

d.

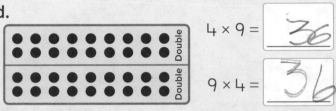

$4 \times 9 = 36$

$9 \times 4 = 36$

double 36 is 72

double 72 is 144

3. Complete the equation. Then write the turnaround fact to match.

a.

$4 \times 7 = 26$

$7 \times 4 = 28$

b.

$4 \times 3 = 12$

$10 \times 10 = 100$

c.

$10 \times 4 = 40$

$12 \times 12 = 144$

Step Ahead

Color the ⬭ beside the thinking you could use to figure
out the product. Then complete the equation.

a.

$4 \times 5 = \underline{\hspace{1cm}}$

- ⬭ double 4 is 8, double 8 is 16
- ⬭ double 5 is 10, double 10 is 20
- ⬭ double 4 is 8, double 5 is 10

b.

$9 \times 4 = \underline{\hspace{1cm}}$

- ⬭ double 9 is 18, double 18 is 36
- ⬭ double 9 is 18, double 4 is 8
- ⬭ double 4 is 8, double 8 is 16

Think and Solve The numbers in the circles are the sums of the rows and columns.

A	A	(18)
B	C	(12)
B	A	(16)
(23)	(23)	

For example, B + A = 16.
Same letters are the same numbers.

A = ☐   B = ☐   C = ☐

Start with a row or column that has all the same letters.

Words at Work

Imagine your friend was away from school when you learned about using the **double-double strategy** for the fours multiplication facts. Write how you would explain the strategy to your friend.

_____

_____

_____

_____

_____

_____

_____

_____

_____

1. Each large shape is one whole. Use a ruler to draw lines to connect shapes that show the same fraction shaded.

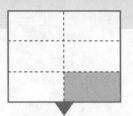  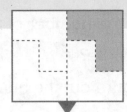 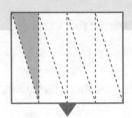

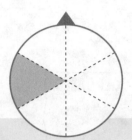 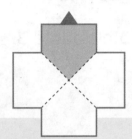 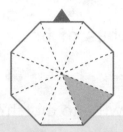 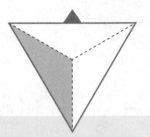

2. Draw a picture to match each equation.

a.	b.
$2 \times 4 = 8$	$6 \times 2 = 12$

Write the multiplication fact and its turnaround fact to match each picture.

a.

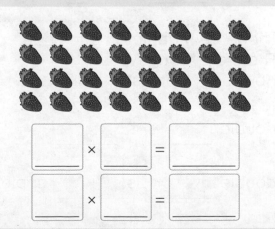

☐ × ☐ = ☐

☐ × ☐ = ☐

b.

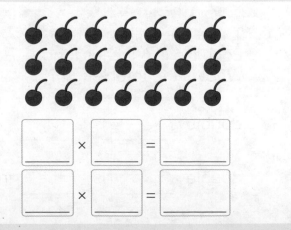

☐ × ☐ = ☐

☐ × ☐ = ☐

FROM 2.12.6

FROM 3.3.2

Step In   These tennis balls are sold in tubes of three.

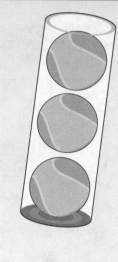

How could you figure out the number of tennis balls in two tubes?

What equation could you write?

What is an easy way to figure out the number of tennis balls in four tubes?

> Two tubes of 3 balls is double 3
> so
> four tubes of balls is double double 3.

What equation could you write to match?

Golf balls are sold in bags of five.
How could you figure out the number of balls in four bags?

GOLF BALLS

Step Up   1. Use the **double-double strategy** to solve each problem.

a. There are 7 people in each car.
    There are 4 cars.
    How many people in total?

double [7] is [14]

double [14] is [   ] people

b. There are 4 shelves.
    10 books are on each shelf.
    How many books in total?

double [   ] is [   ]

double [   ] is [   ] books

c. There are 4 tiles.
    Each tile is 6 inches long.
    What is the total length?

double [   ] is [   ]

double [   ] is [   ] inches

d. There are 9 apples in each bag.
    There are 4 bags.
    How many apples in total?

double [   ] is [   ]

double [   ] is [   ] apples

2. Write a single-digit number in the first box. Then write the double and the double double.

a.

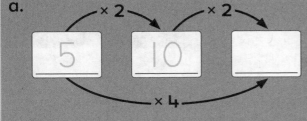

b.

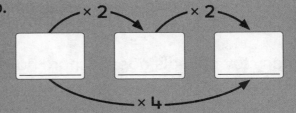

c.

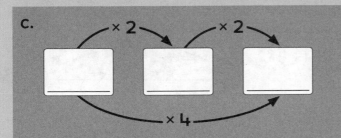

d.

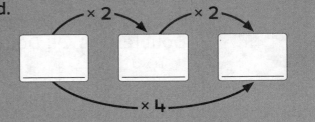

3. Write numbers in the diagram to help solve the word problem.

Dena earns $6 each week. How much money could she have after 4 weeks?

$ _____

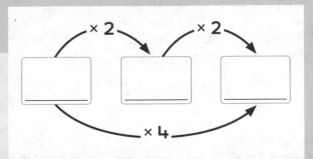

4. Write the products. Think double double. Then write the turnaround.

a.

5 × 4 = _____

_____ × _____ = _____

b.

3 × 4 = _____

_____ × _____ = _____

c.

8 × 4 = _____

_____ × _____ = _____

Step Ahead

Write a number between 10 and 20 in the first box. Then write the double and the double double.

a.

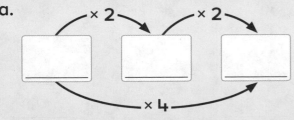

b.

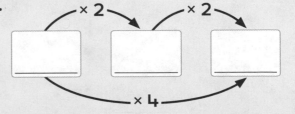

Step In

This bag holds 12 toy animals.
Richard buys 4 bags.

TOY DINOSAURS

How many toy animals does Richard have in total?
How do you know?

I could use a doubles strategy.
Double 12 is 24. Double 24 is 48.

How did you figure out each double?

The bags cost $16 each.

Complete this diagram to
figure out the total cost.

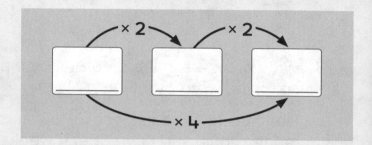

Step Up

1. Calculate the cost of buying four of each item. Show your thinking.

a.

BLOCKS $11

$ _____

b.

 $25

$ _____

c.

 $15

$ _____

2. Think double double to write the products. Then write the turnaround.
You can show your thinking on page 118.

a.
13 × 4 = _____

_____ × _____ = _____

b.
4 × 26 = _____

_____ × _____ = _____

c.
4 × 32 = _____

_____ × _____ = _____

d.
19 × 4 = _____

_____ × _____ = _____

3. Write a two-digit number in the first box. Then write the double and the double double. You can show your thinking on page 118.

a.

b.
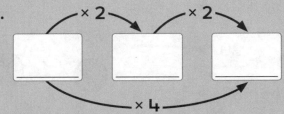

c.
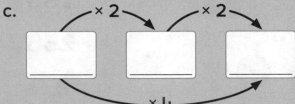

d.
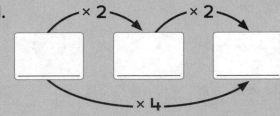

Step Ahead   Solve this problem. Show your thinking.

Deana buys two tickets that cost $17 each. Marcos buys four tickets that each cost $14. What is the difference between the total amount they each pay?

$_____

Computation Practice

What is black and white and blue?

★ Use a ruler to draw a straight line to the correct total. The line will pass through a letter. Write each letter above its matching total at the bottom of the page.

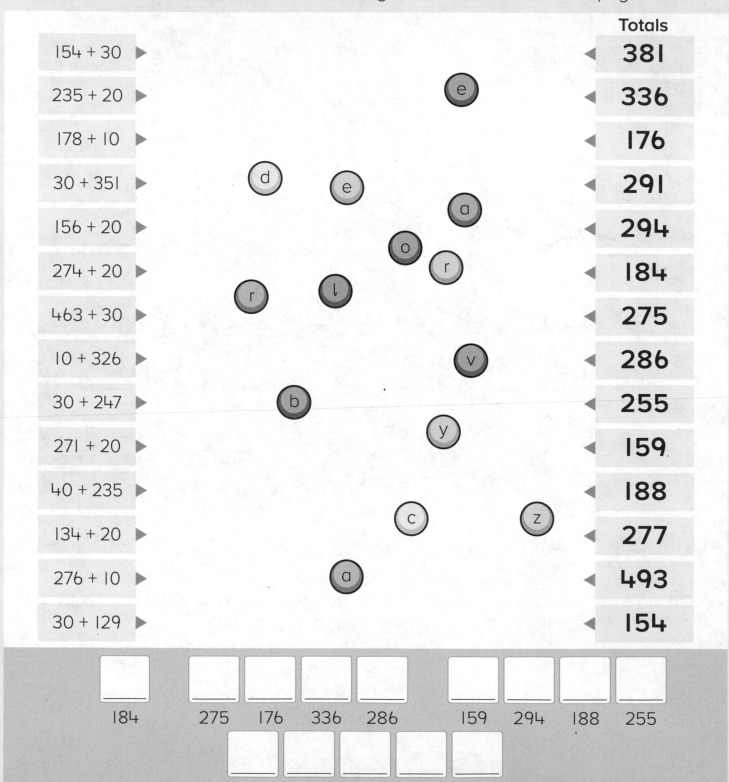

Equations		Totals
154 + 30 ▶		◀ **381**
235 + 20 ▶		◀ **336**
178 + 10 ▶		◀ **176**
30 + 351 ▶		◀ **291**
156 + 20 ▶		◀ **294**
274 + 20 ▶		◀ **184**
463 + 30 ▶		◀ **275**
10 + 326 ▶		◀ **286**
30 + 247 ▶		◀ **255**
271 + 20 ▶		◀ **159**
40 + 235 ▶		◀ **188**
134 + 20 ▶		◀ **277**
276 + 10 ▶		◀ **493**
30 + 129 ▶		◀ **154**

Letters in diagram: e, d, e, a, o, r, r, l, v, b, y, c, z, a

184 275 176 336 286   159 294 188 255

277 381 493 291 154

© ORIGO Education

Ongoing Practice

I. Circle the pyramids.

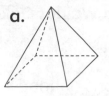
a.

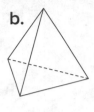
b.

c.

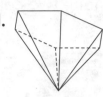
d.

e.

f.

g.

2. Write the missing numbers.

a.
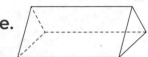
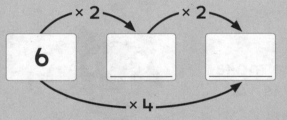
6

b.
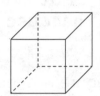
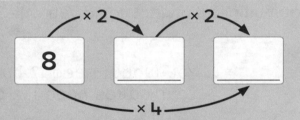
8

c.
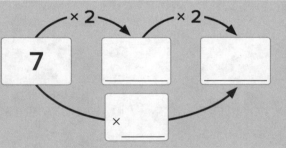
7
×

d.
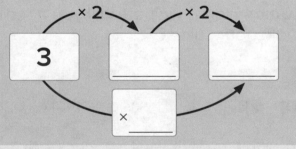
3
×

Preparing for Module 4

Complete these equations.

a.
$6 \times 10 = \underline{}$

b.
$10 \times 2 = \underline{}$

c.
$9 \times 10 = \underline{}$

d.
$10 \times \underline{} = 40$

e.
$\underline{} \times 3 = 30$

f.
$10 \times 8 = \underline{}$

g.
$\underline{} \times 10 = 10$

h.
$10 \times \underline{} = 50$

i.
$\underline{} \times 7 = 70$

Step In   This recipe makes one cake.

How many bananas would you need
to make two cakes?

That is 6 bananas
because double 3 is 6.

How could you figure out the number
of bananas needed to make four cakes?

Banana and Walnut Cake

3 bananas

4 teaspoons of honey

2 cups of flour

1 cup of milk

12 large walnuts

What multiplication fact could you write?

You would need 12 bananas to make
four cakes because double 6 is 12.

How many large walnuts will you need
to make four cakes?

Step Up   1. This recipe makes one large bowl of fruit gelatin. Write the answers.

a. How many sliced peaches are
    needed to make four bowls
    of fruit gelatin?

b. Hailey bought 20 strawberries.
    How many bowls of fruit gelatin
    could she make?

Fruit Gelatin

1 packet of gelatin

2 sliced peaches

10 strawberries

1 can of pineapple

4 bananas

c. How many cans of pineapple
    are needed to make four
    bowls of fruit gelatin?

d. Andre has 16 bananas.
    How many bowls of fruit gelatin
    could he make?

2. Write an equation to match each story. Write a **?** to show the unknown amount.

a. 6 eggs are placed in each carton.
There are 4 cartons.
How many eggs are there in total?

_____

b. Cans are stacked in 2 equal rows.
There are 7 cans in each row.
How many cans are in the stack?

_____

c. 9 pickup trucks are parked end to
end. Each pickup is 4 meters long.
What is the total length of the
pickup trucks?

_____

d. Pictures on a wall are in 2 rows and
8 columns. How many pictures are
on the wall?

_____

3. Solve each problem. Show your thinking.

a. Katherine buys 2 T-shirts for $16
each and 1 pair of socks for $4.
How much did she spend?

$_____

b. There are 4 bags of toys. Each
bag has 15 red and 25 blue toys
How many toys are there in all?

_____ toys

| Step Ahead | Look at this tile pattern. Write in words how you could figure out the total number of blue triangles without counting one at a time. |

_____

_____

_____

_____

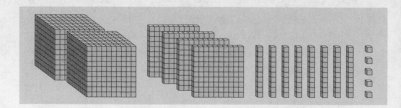

Step In   What number do these blocks show?

Write the number on this expander.

How do you read the number?

Now add 10. Write the new number.

thousands

Now subtract 100. Write the new number.

thousands

What number is represented by these blocks?

What number is 100 greater? What number is 100 less?

What number is 10 greater? What number is 10 less?

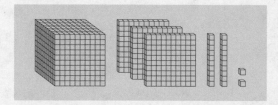

Step Up   1. Write the numbers that are 100 greater and 100 less.

100 less						
	2,359	842	1,206	506	5,101	8,995
100 greater						

2. Write the numbers that are 10 greater and 10 less.

10 less						
	670	4,375	1,416	805	7,395	9,985
10 greater						

3. Your teacher will give you a labeled number cube.
Follow these steps to complete the number trail.

   a. Roll the cube. Write the number in the first box.

   b. Repeat the above step for each box on the trail.

   c. Then add or subtract along the trail. Write the missing numbers
   in the hexagons.

5,762 → + _____ → ⬡ → − _____ → ⬡

+ _____

⬡ ← − _____ ← ⬡ ← + _____ ← ⬡

− _____

⬡ → + _____ → ⬡ → − _____ → ⬡

Step Ahead

The number cube from Question 3 was used with these number trails. Write the missing numbers.

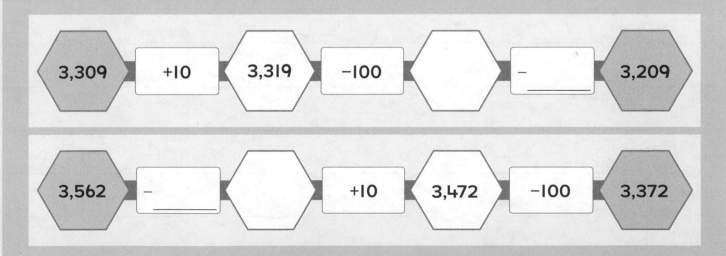

3,309 → +10 → 3,319 → −100 → ⬡ → − _____ → 3,209

3,562 → − _____ → ⬡ → +10 → 3,472 → −100 → 3,372

© ORIGO Education

Think and Solve THINK TANK   The blue whale is 27 m long.

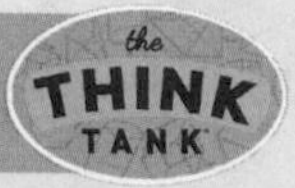

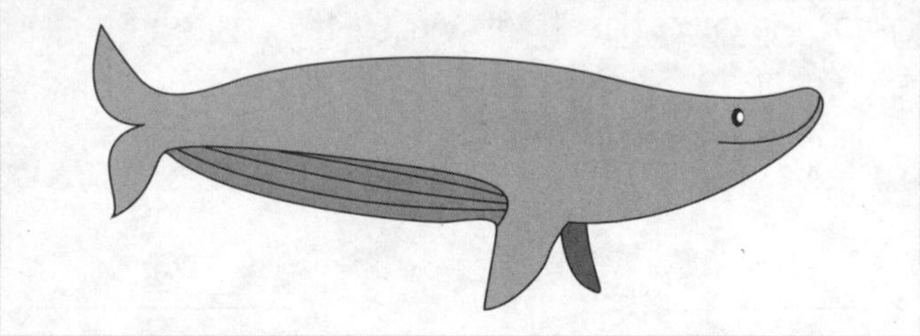

The humpback whale is 6 m **longer** than the orca whale.
The orca whale is 20 m **shorter** than the blue whale.

Write the missing numbers.

a.

The humpback whale is _____ m.

b.

The orca whale is _____ m.

Words at Work   Write in words how you solve this problem.

There are six motorcycles and a number of cars in the parking lot.
If there are 48 wheels in total, how many cars are in the parking lot?

Ongoing Practice

I. A 3D object with all flat faces is called a **polyhedron**. Circle the polyhedrons.

a.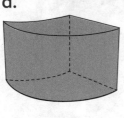

b.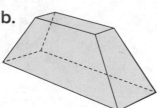

c.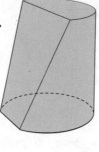

d.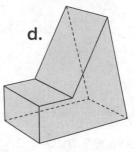

2. Write an equation to match each story. Use a **?** to show the unknown amount.

a. Samuel's mom bought 3 tickets for the roller coaster. Tickets are $4 each. What was the total cost?

_____

b. Each car on the roller coaster holds 4 people. There are 6 cars. How many people does it carry?

_____

c. One ride on the roller coaster takes 3 minutes. How long would 2 rides take?

_____

d. Each roller coaster car is 2 meters long. What is the total length of 6 roller coaster cars?

_____

Preparing for Module 4   Complete these equations.

a. $5 \times \boxed{} = 20$

b. $\boxed{} \times 3 = 15$

c. $5 \times 8 = \boxed{}$

d. $\boxed{} \times 5 = 5$

e. $5 \times \boxed{} = 25$

f. $5 \times 7 = \boxed{}$

g. $6 \times 5 = \boxed{}$

h. $5 \times 2 = \boxed{}$

i. $9 \times 5 = \boxed{}$

Step In

Sara measured the distance around the trunks of some huge trees in a forest. This distance is called the girth.

Tree	Girth (cm)
A	311
B	265
C	342
D	270

Which tree had the greatest girth? How do you know?

What symbols are used to show **greater than** and **less than**?

What does each sentence below tell you about the pair of numbers?

172 > 149   196 < 201   325 < 342   489 > 398

Step Up

1. Write the number that should be in the position shown by each arrow. Think carefully before you write.

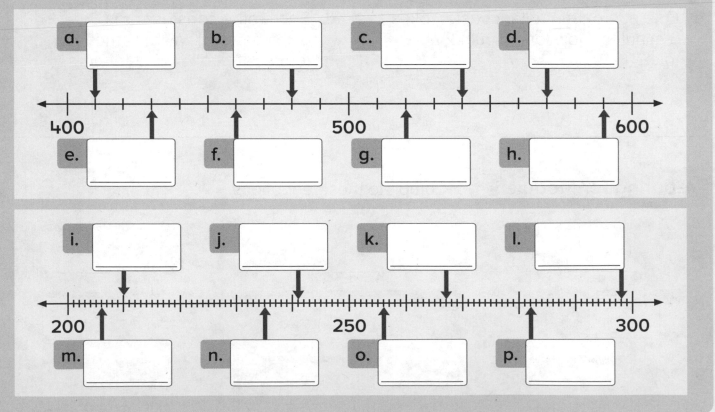

2. Draw a line to join each number to its position on the number line.
Then write **<** or **>** in each circle to describe each pair of numbers.

a. 253 ◯ 256   **b.** 261 ◯ 257   **c.** 264 ◯ 268

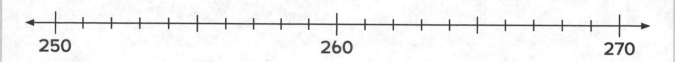

250   260   270

d. 607 ◯ 612   **e.** 634 ◯ 649   **f.** 690 ◯ 684

600   650   700

3. Write each set of numbers in order from **least** to **greatest**.

a. 356   605   538

☐ ☐ ☐

b. 402   176   248

☐ ☐ ☐

c. 703   741   725   767

☐ ☐ ☐ ☐

Step Ahead

a. Use only these digits. Write all the different three-digit numbers that are possible.   **8** **3** **1**

☐

b. Rewrite your numbers in order from **greatest** to **least**.

☐

Step In How can you figure out which number is greater?

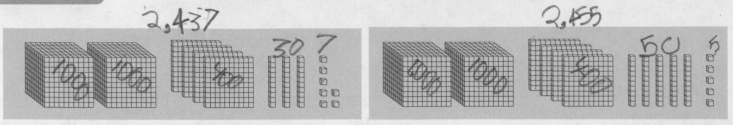

2,437   30 7   2,455   50 5

Which place would you look at first to mark the numbers on this number line?

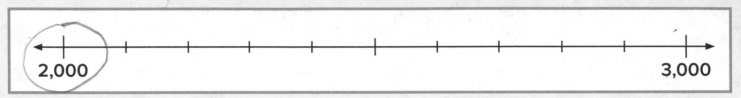

2,000   3,000

Use a different color to show your estimate of the position of each number on the line.

How can you tell which number is greater?

Which of these numbers is greater? How do you know?   906 ⟨ 2,074

Write **<** or **>** to complete the statement.

Step Up   Use this table to answer Questions 1, 2, and 3 on page 109.

Mountain Heights	
Name	**Height (meters)**
Cheaha Mountain	736
Mount Washburn	3,116
Mount Magazine	839
Borah Peak	3,861
Mount Elbert	4,401
Mount Whitney	4,421
Mount Greylock	1,064
Eagle Mountain	701

1. Write the height of each mountain.
Then write **is less than** or **is greater than** to make the statement true.

a. Borah Peak   Mount Greylock

3,861 m   *is greater than*   1,064 m

b. Eagle Mountain   Mount Washburn

701 m   *is less than*   4,421 m

2. Write the height of each mountain. Then write **<** or **>** to make the statement true.

a. Mount Magazine   Mount Greylock

839 m < 1,064 m

b. Mount Magazine   Borah Peak

839 m < 3,861 m

c. Mount Whitney   Cheaha Mountain

4,421 m < 7,36 m

d. Borah Peak   Mount Washburn

3,861 m > 3,116 m

e. Mount Elbert   Mount Whitney

4,401 m < 4,421 m

f. Mount Washburn   Mount Elbert

3,116 m < 4,401 m

3. Write the mountain heights in order from **greatest** to **least**.

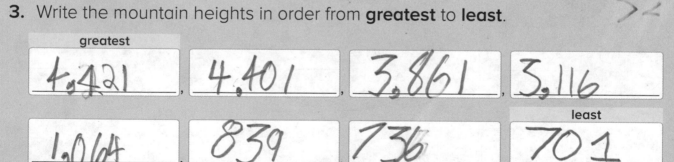

greatest

4,421 , 4,401 , 3,861 , 3,116

1,064 , 839 , 736 , 701

least

Step Ahead   In each pair, circle the number that is greater.

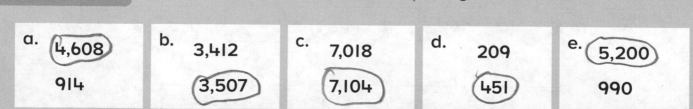

a. (4,608)   **b.** 3,412   **c.** 7,018   **d.** 209   **e.** (5,200)

914   (3,507)   (7,104)   (451)   990

Computation Practice

How many eggs does a peacock lay in one year?

★ Complete the equations. Then write each letter above its matching difference at the bottom of the page. Some letters appear more than once.

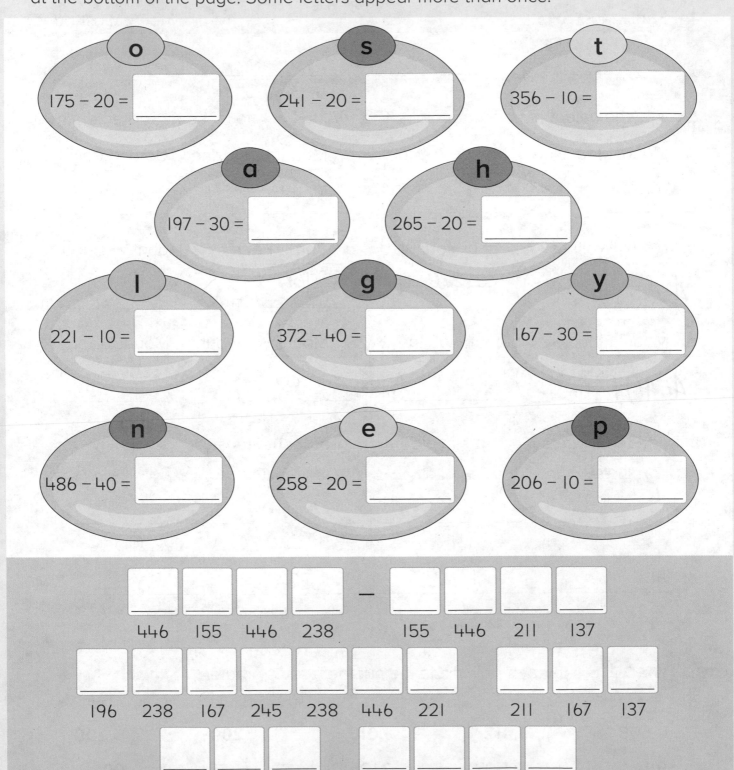

o $175 - 20 =$ ____

s $241 - 20 =$ ____

t $356 - 10 =$ ____

a $197 - 30 =$ ____

h $265 - 20 =$ ____

l $221 - 10 =$ ____

g $372 - 40 =$ ____

y $167 - 30 =$ ____

n $486 - 40 =$ ____

e $258 - 20 =$ ____

p $206 - 10 =$ ____

446   155   446   238   —   155   446   211   137

196   238   167   245   238   446   221   211   167   137

346   245   238   238   332   332   221

Ongoing Practice

1. Draw lines between dots to split each shape into **three** rectangles

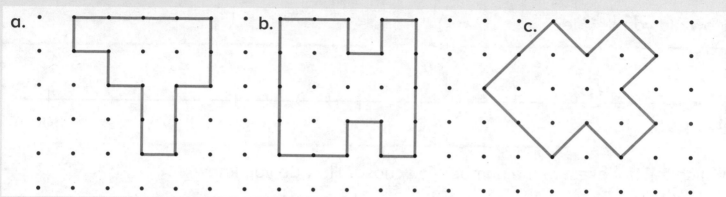

2. a. Write the numbers that are 10 less and 10 greater.

10 less						
	2,049	1,395	2,601	4,097	3,006	5,991
10 greater						

b. Write the numbers that are 100 less and 100 greater.

100 less						
	1,492	2,316	4,709	4,038	1,950	7,099
100 greater						

Preparing for Module 4   Use a doubling strategy to complete this table.

	Number	Double (×2)	Double Double (×4)
a.	5	10	
b.	8		
c.	6		
d.	3		

Step In

What number do you think the arrow is pointing to on the number line?

How did you decide?

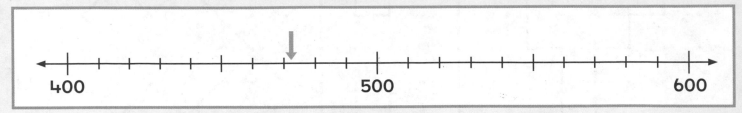

400   500   600

Which ten is closest to the number you chose? How do you know?

Which hundred is closest to the number you chose? How did you figure it out?

I think the number is 473. The closest ten is 470 because it is a shorter jump from 473 to 470 than to 480.

Rounding a number to the nearest ten means finding the ten that is closest to that number.

So 364 rounded to the nearest ten is 360, and 367 rounded to the nearest ten is 370.

How would you round a number that is halfway between two tens? ... two hundreds?

Step Up   1. Look at the number line below.

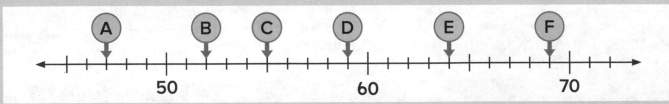

50   60   70

For each arrow on the number line, write the number in the table below.

Then write the nearest **ten** for each number.

Arrow	A	B	C	D	E	F
Number						
Nearest ten						

2. For each arrow on the number line, write the number in the table.
Then write the nearest ten and nearest hundred for each number.

Arrow	A	B	C	D	E	F
Number						
Nearest ten						
Nearest hundred						

3. Round each number to the nearest **ten**.

a. 164 _160_

b. 593 _590_

c. 475 _470_

d. 604 _600_

e. 218 _220_

f. 96 _100_

4. Round each number to the nearest **hundred**.

a. 670 _700_

b. 413 _400_

c. 788 _800_

d. 310 _300_

e. 251 _300_

f. 650 _600_

Step Ahead

a. Imagine you rounded a number to the nearest ten
and your answer was 480. Write 4 different starting numbers.

_____ , _____ , _____ , _____

b. Imagine you rounded a number to the nearest hundred
and your answer was 600. Write 4 different starting numbers.

_____ , _____ , _____ , _____

Step In

How would you round the distance from
Los Angeles to Sydney to the nearest 10 miles?

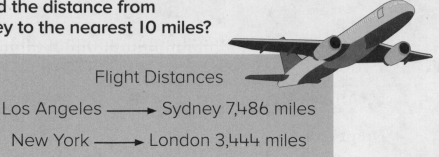

Flight Distances

Los Angeles ⟶ Sydney 7,486 miles

New York ⟶ London 3,444 miles

Kay uses a number line.

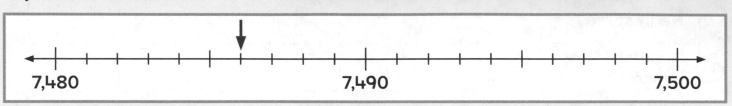

7,480   7,490   7,500

How does the number line help her thinking?

Logan thinks about place value. He follows these steps.

7,4⑧6	7,4⑧6	7,4⑧6
First he finds the place to which he is rounding.	Then he looks at the next lowest place value.	If the digit in that place is greater than or equal to 5 then the number is rounded up.

How could you use Logan's strategy to round the distance from
New York to London to the nearest **hundred** miles?

This time the digit to the right of the
rounding place is less than 5. So, the
distance is rounded down to 3,400 miles.

Step Up

1. Show the position of the distance on the number line.
Then round the distance to the nearest **hundred** miles.

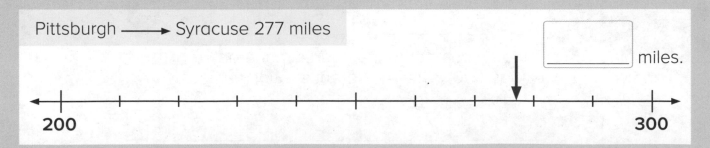

Pittsburgh ⟶ Syracuse 277 miles

_____ miles.

200   300

2. Show the position of each number on the number line.
Then round each number to the nearest **ten** and **hundred**.

a.

1,437

1,400   1,500

Nearest ten _____

Nearest hundred _____

b.

4,862

4,800   4,900

Nearest ten _____

Nearest hundred _____

3. Round each number to the nearest **ten**.

a. 832 _____

b. 389 _____

c. 745 _____

d. 3,672 _____

e. 7,817 _____

f. 5,356 _____

4. Round each number to the nearest **hundred**.

a. 493 _____

b. 238 _____

c. 647 _____

d. 2,809 _____

e. 4,376 _____

f. 9,060 _____

Step Ahead

Show the position of each number on the number line.
Then round each number to the nearest **thousand**.

6,000   7,000

6,340 _____

6,400 _____

6,510 _____

6,890 _____

Think and Solve

Same shapes weigh the same. Write the missing value inside each shape.

Words at Work

Choose and write words from the list to complete these sentences. Some words are not used. One word is used more than once.

| ninety |
| hundred |
| sixteen |
| rounding |
| twelve |
| one |
| twenty |

a. _____ is double double 4.

b. Double six is _____.

c. _____ a number to the nearest ten means finding the ten that is closest to that number.

d. Double double three is _____.

e. The closest hundred to 96 is _____ hundred.

f. The closest ten to 96 is one _____.

1. Cooper wants to make rhombuses with groups of straws. Count and measure the straws in each group below and color the ◯ beside the correct answer.

a.

○ Can make a rhombus.
○ Can't make a rhombus.

b.

○ Can make a rhombus.
○ Can't make a rhombus.

2. Write **how far away** each number is from the nearest hundred. You can draw lines to help you.

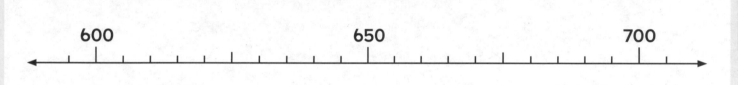

600   650   700

a.
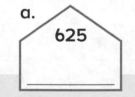
625
_____

b.
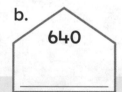
640
_____

c.
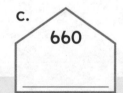
660
_____

d.
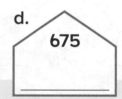
675
_____

e.
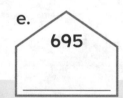
695
_____

Preparing for Module 4

Color one part of each strip red. Then write the fraction that is red.

a.

[strip divided into parts]   [box] _____

b.

[strip divided into parts]   [box] _____

c.

[strip divided into parts]   [box] _____

Step In

Mana and James each bought a fishbowl. They also bought 10 goldfish to share.

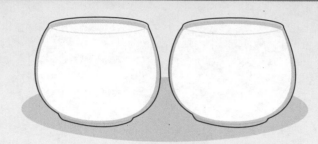

Draw goldfish to show the same number of fish in each bowl.

What word story could you write to describe the sharing?

10 goldfish shared between 2 bowls is 5 goldfish in each bowl.

What number sentence could you write to describe the sharing?

The symbol ÷ is used for division. The result of division is called the **quotient**.

Mana and James decide to put only two goldfish in each fishbowl.

How many fishbowls will they need for the 10 fish?

Now we know the number in each bowl, but we do not know the number of bowls.

What picture could you draw to match?

What word story could you tell to describe the grouping?

What equation could you write to describe the grouping?

Step Up

1. Read the story. Then write the number in each equal group or the number of equal groups. Use cubes to help your thinking.

a. There are 18 students in total. There are 9 tents.

There are ____ students in each tent.

b. There are 30 birds in total. There are 10 birds in each cage.

There are ____ cages.

2. Write the missing numbers. You can share tens and ones blocks to help your thinking.

a.

16 shared by 2 is _____ each.

16 ÷ 2 = _____

b.

40 shared by 5 is _____ each.

40 ÷ 5 = _____

c.

60 shared by 10 is _____ each.

60 ÷ 10 = _____

d.

28 shared by 4 is _____ each.

28 ÷ 4 = _____

3. Complete these. You can share tens and ones blocks to help your thinking.

a.

35 in groups of 5 is _____ groups.

35 ÷ 5 = _____

b.

8 in groups of 2 is _____ groups.

8 ÷ 2 = _____

c.

50 in groups of 10 is _____ groups.

50 ÷ 10 = _____

d.

32 in groups of 4 is _____ groups.

32 ÷ 4 = _____

e.

24 in groups of 4 is _____ groups.

24 ÷ 4 = _____

f.

25 in groups of 5 is _____ groups.

25 ÷ 5 = _____

Step Ahead

Use these numbers to make each story true. Each number can only be used once.

10 5 6 35 7 60

a.

There were _____ carrot sticks.

_____ friends shared them equally.

Each person has _____ carrot sticks.

b.

There are _____ cans in total.

Each box holds _____ cans.

There are _____ boxes.

Step In How could you describe this picture of apples?

What multiplication facts could you write?

☐ × ☐ = ☐   ☐ × ☐ = ☐

Imagine the apples are packed into bags of 4.
How many bags could you fill?

What division fact could you write?

☐ ÷ ☐ = ☐

Imagine the apples are packed equally into 5 bags.
How many apples will be in each bag?

What division fact could you write?

☐ ÷ ☐ = ☐

> You can write 2 multiplication facts and 2 division facts for any array picture.
>
> These 4 facts are called a **fact family** because they are related.

Step Up   1.   Write the fact family for each array.

a.
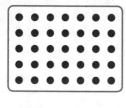

___ × ___ = ___

___ × ___ = ___

___ ÷ ___ = ___

___ ÷ ___ = ___

b.

___ × ___ = ___

___ × ___ = ___

___ ÷ ___ = ___

___ ÷ ___ = ___

c.

___ × ___ = ___

___ × ___ = ___

___ ÷ ___ = ___

___ ÷ ___ = ___

d.
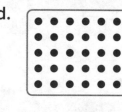

___ × ___ = ___

___ × ___ = ___

___ ÷ ___ = ___

___ ÷ ___ = ___

ORIGO Stepping Stones · Grade 3 · 4.2

© ORIGO Education

2. Color an array to match the numbers given. Then complete the fact family.

a.

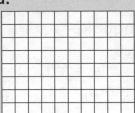

$5 \times 2 = $ _____

_____ $\times$ _____ $=$ _____

_____ $\div$ _____ $=$ _____

_____ $\div$ _____ $=$ _____

b.

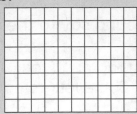

$4 \times 10 = $ _____

_____ $\times$ _____ $=$ _____

_____ $\div$ _____ $=$ _____

_____ $\div$ _____ $=$ _____

c.

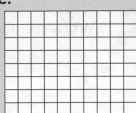

$2 \times 9 = $ _____

_____ $\times$ _____ $=$ _____

_____ $\div$ _____ $=$ _____

_____ $\div$ _____ $=$ _____

d.

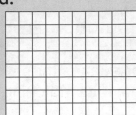

$5 \times 9 = $ _____

_____ $\times$ _____ $=$ _____

_____ $\div$ _____ $=$ _____

_____ $\div$ _____ $=$ _____

3. Complete the equations. Then shade each fact, using the same color for facts that belong in the same fact family.

$12 \div 2 = \boxed{}$ $3 \times \boxed{} = 30$ $12 \div \boxed{} = 2$ $\boxed{} = 5 \times 4$

$\boxed{} = 10 \times 3$ $20 \div 5 = \boxed{}$ $\boxed{} = 6 \times 2$ $7 \times 5 = \boxed{}$

$30 \div 3 = \boxed{}$ $\boxed{} = 35 \div 5$ $20 \div 4 = \boxed{}$ $\boxed{} = 2 \times 6$

Step Ahead   Color an array to match each fact. Then complete the equations.

a.

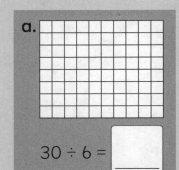

$30 \div 6 = $

b.

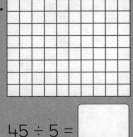

$45 \div 5 = $ _____

c.

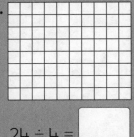

$24 \div 4 = $ _____

d.

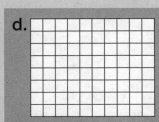

$16 \div 2 = $ _____

Computation Practice   **What did the ground say to the earthquake?**

★ For each of these, write the product and the turnaround fact. Then write each letter above its matching product in the grid below. Some letters appear more than once.

4 × 2 = ☐ = ☐ × ☐   **o**

2 × 6 = ☐ = ☐ × ☐   **a**

2 × 8 = ☐ = ☐ × ☐   **e**

3 × 2 = ☐ = ☐ × ☐   **p**

10 × 2 = ☐ = ☐ × ☐   **r**

7 × 2 = ☐ = ☐ × ☐   **u**

2 × 9 = ☐ = ☐ × ☐   **k**

2 × 5 = ☐ = ☐ × ☐   **y**

1 × 2 = ☐ = ☐ × ☐   **c**

2 × 2 = ☐ = ☐ × ☐   **m**

☐ ☐ ☐   ☐ ☐ ☐ ☐ ☐
10 8 14   2 20 12 2 18

☐ ☐   ☐ ☐
4 16   14 6

Complete these facts as fast as you can.

5 × 7 = ☐   5 × 5 = ☐   5 × 3 = ☐

8 × 5 = ☐   5 × 4 = ☐   5 × 1 = ☐

6 × 5 = ☐   2 × 5 = ☐   9 × 5 = ☐

ORIGO Stepping Stones · Grade 3 · 4.2

© ORIGO Education

Ongoing Practice

1. Write the number of hundreds, tens, and ones.
Then write an equation to show the total.
You can use blocks to help.

a. 325 + 68

There are ☐ hundreds.

There are ☐ tens.

There are ☐ ones.

_____ + _____ + _____ = _____

b. 473 + 95

There are ☐ hundreds.

There are ☐ tens.

There are ☐ ones.

_____ + _____ + _____ = _____

2. Complete each of these. Use tens and ones blocks to help your thinking.

a.

28 in groups of 4 is ☐ groups

28 ÷ 4 = ☐

b.

16 in groups of 2 is ☐ groups

16 ÷ 2 = ☐

c.

30 in groups of 5 is ☐ groups

30 ÷ 5 = ☐

d.

20 in groups of 4 is ☐ groups

20 ÷ 4 = ☐

Preparing for Module 5

Draw more dots to show a double double.
Then complete the equations.

a.

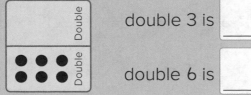

double 3 is ☐

double 6 is ☐

$4 \times 3 = $ ☐ $= 3 \times 4$

b.

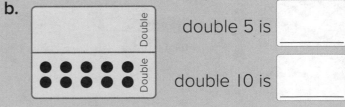

double 5 is ☐

double 10 is ☐

☐ $\times 5 = $ ☐ $= 5 \times$ ☐

Step In

This is a sheet of 40 stickers.

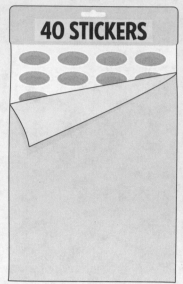

40 STICKERS

How could you figure out the number of rows?

What equations could you write?

There are 40 stickers in total. There are 4 stickers in each row. 40 ÷ 4 = ?

There are 40 stickers in total. There are 4 stickers in each row. 4 × ? = 40

To solve a division fact it is often easier to think of the related multiplication fact.

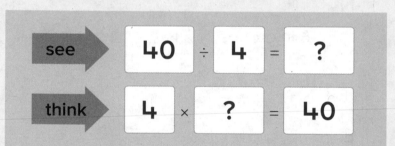

see → | 40 | ÷ | 4 | = | ? |

think → | 4 | × | ? | = | 40 |

How many rows are there?

What multiplication fact could you use to figure out 50 ÷ 5?

Step Up

1. Complete the multiplication fact you would use to figure out the division fact. Then complete the division fact.

a.

30 dots in total

3 × ▢ = 30   30 ÷ 3 = ▢

b.

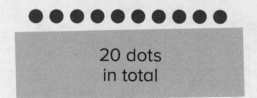

20 dots in total

▢ × 10 = 20   20 ÷ 10 = ▢

2. Complete these facts.

a.

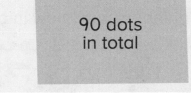

60 dots in total

$6 \times \boxed{} = 60 \qquad 60 \div 6 = \underline{}$

b.

● ● ● ● ● ● ● ● ● ●

80 dots in total

$\boxed{} \times 8 = 80 \qquad 80 \div 8 = \underline{}$

c.

70 dots in total

$7 \times \boxed{} = 70 \qquad 70 \div 7 = \underline{}$

d.

● ● ● ● ● ● ● ● ● ●

90 dots in total

$\boxed{} \times 10 = 90 \qquad 90 \div 10 = \underline{}$

3. Write a multiplication fact and division fact to match each problem. Use a **?** to show the unknown amount.

a. 4 students fit in each canoe. There are 40 students. How many canoes are needed?

_____ × _____ = _____

_____ ÷ _____ = _____

b. 80 DVDs are placed in 10 equal stacks. How many DVDs are in each stack?

_____ × _____ = _____

_____ ÷ _____ = _____

c. 50 connecting cubes are joined in stacks of 10. How many stacks are there?

_____ × _____ = _____

_____ ÷ _____ = _____

Step Ahead

How many $10 bills could you trade for all of these bills?

$\boxed{}$

Step In   What do you know about this array?

How could you figure out the number of dots in each row?

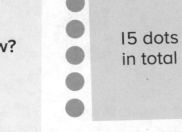

15 dots in total

5 rows of some number is equal to 15.

Write the two numbers you know in each of these equations.

☐ × ☐ = ☐   ☐ ÷ ☐ = ☐

Now write the missing numbers.

What do you know about this array?
How could you figure out the number of equal rows?

30 dots in total

Write the two numbers you know in each fact,
then write the missing numbers.

☐ × ☐ = ☐   ☐ ÷ ☐ = ☐

Step Up   1.   Complete the multiplication fact you would use to figure out
the division fact. Then complete the division fact.

a.

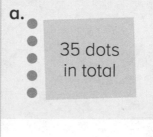

35 dots in total

5 × _____ = 35

35 ÷ 5 = _____

b.

20 dots in total

_____ × 4 = 20

20 ÷ 4 = _____

c.

20 dots in total

5 × _____ = 20

20 ÷ 5 = _____

d.

10 dots in total

_____ × 5 = 10

10 ÷ 5 = _____

2. Complete these facts.

a.

25 dots in total

_____ × 5 = 25

25 ÷ 5 = _____

b.

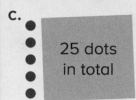

30 dots in total

6 × _____ = 30

30 ÷ 6 = _____

c.

25 dots in total

5 × _____ = 25

25 ÷ 5 = _____

d.

40 dots in total

_____ × 5 = 40

40 ÷ 5 = _____

e.

15 dots in total

_____ × _____ = 15

15 ÷ _____ = _____

f.

45 dots in total

_____ × _____ = 45

45 ÷ _____ = _____

g.

35 dots in total

_____ × _____ = 35

35 ÷ _____ = _____

h.

50 dots in total

_____ × _____ = 50

50 ÷ _____ = _____

3. Write a multiplication fact and division fact to match each problem. Use a **?** to show the unknown amount.

a. A rope is 15 meters long. It is cut into 3 equal lengths. How long is each piece?

_____ × _____ = _____

_____ ÷ _____ = _____

b. Gemma trades some $5 bills for a $20 bill. How many $5 bills did she trade?

_____ × _____ = _____

_____ ÷ _____ = _____

c. 30 stickers are printed in 6 equal columns. How many rows are there?

_____ × _____ = _____

_____ ÷ _____ = _____

Step Ahead   How many $5 bills could you trade for all of these bills?

Think and Solve Read the directions first.

a. Use a ruler to draw a line to make two parts the **same** size and shape.

The sum of the numbers in each part must be the same.

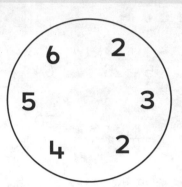

b. Use a ruler to draw two lines to make four parts the **same** size and shape.

The sum of the numbers in each part must be the same.

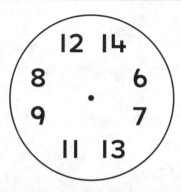

Words at Work

a. Write the multiplication fact family that uses 5 and 6.

b. Then write about how the multiplication and division facts are related.

___ × ___ = ___

___ × ___ = ___

___ ÷ ___ = ___

___ ÷ ___ = ___

Ongoing Practice

I. Calculate each sum.

a.

H	T	O
1	6	7
+ 1	1	6
	1	3
	7	0
2	0	0

b.

H	T	O
	4	8	4
+	3	7	1

c.

H	T	O
	3	9	2
+	1	4	7

2. Write the fact family for each array.

a.

_____ × _____ = _____

_____ × _____ = _____

_____ ÷ _____ = _____

_____ ÷ _____ = _____

b.

_____ × _____ = _____

_____ × _____ = _____

_____ ÷ _____ = _____

_____ ÷ _____ = _____

c.
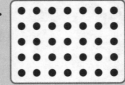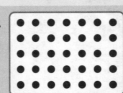

_____ × _____ = _____

_____ × _____ = _____

_____ ÷ _____ = _____

_____ ÷ _____ = _____

d.

_____ × _____ = _____

_____ × _____ = _____

_____ ÷ _____ = _____

_____ ÷ _____ = _____

Preparing for Module 5

Write the missing numbers.

a.

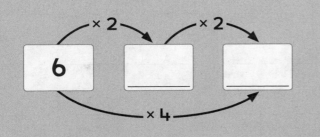

6 → × 2 → _____ → × 2 → _____
6 → × 4 →

b.

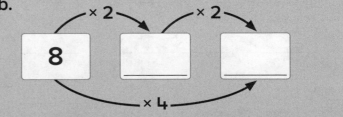

8 → × 2 → _____ → × 2 → _____
8 → × 4 →

Step In

How could you figure out the total number of dots in this array?

What multiplication facts could you write?

There are 6 rows of 10.
6 × 10 = 60 or 10 × 6 = 60

What are the related division facts that complete the fact family?

Write the multiplication and division facts to match this array.

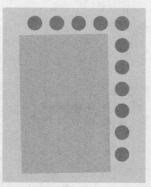

☐ × ☐ = ☐   ☐ × ☐ = ☐

☐ ÷ ☐ = ☐   ☐ ÷ ☐ = ☐

Step Up

1. Use what you can see to help write the complete fact family to match each array.

a.
_____ × _____ = _____

_____ × _____ = _____

_____ ÷ _____ = _____

_____ ÷ _____ = _____

b.
_____ × _____ = _____

_____ × _____ = _____

_____ ÷ _____ = _____

_____ ÷ _____ = _____

c.
_____ × _____ = _____

_____ × _____ = _____

_____ ÷ _____ = _____

_____ ÷ _____ = _____

2. Write the missing numbers to complete each fact family.

a.

$3 \times 5 = 15$

$5 \times 3 = \boxed{}$

$15 \div 3 = 5$

$15 \div \boxed{} = 3$

b.

$\boxed{} \times 10 = 50$

$10 \times 5 = 50$

$50 \div \boxed{} = 10$

$50 \div 10 = \boxed{}$

3. Write the missing number to complete each fact.

a. $\boxed{} \div 10 = 5$

b. $40 \div \boxed{} = 4$

c. $35 \div 5 = \boxed{}$

d. $2 = \boxed{} \div 5$

e. $\boxed{} \div 9 = 10$

f. $30 \div \boxed{} = 6$

4. Write a word problem to match this equation.

$45 \div 9 = ?$

_____

_____

_____

Step Ahead   Write the equation that you would use to solve each problem.

1. a. Ricardo earns $3 each week for doing chores. How much money will he earn in 5 weeks?

_____

b. How many weeks will it take him to earn $30?

_____

2. a. Jessica reads 5 books each week. How many weeks will it take her to read 25 books?

_____

b. How many books will she read in 10 weeks?

_____

Step In   16 blocks are shared equally between two friends.
How many blocks are in each share?

Dividing by 2 is the same
as halving. Half of 16 is 8.

Imagine the same bag of blocks is equally shared among four friends.

How could you figure out the number of blocks in each share?

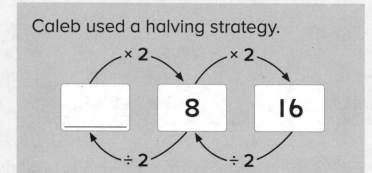

Caleb used a halving strategy.

× 2   × 2

8   16

÷ 2   ÷ 2

Mary thought of the related
multiplication fact.

☐ × 4 = 16

How many blocks are in each share? Write the missing number.

Which strategy do you prefer? Why?

How could you use each strategy to share 24 blocks equally among four friends?

Step Up   1.   Complete the equations to show the number of blocks
in each share. Use cubes to help your thinking.

a.

20 ÷ 2 = ☐

20 ÷ 4 = ☐

20 blocks

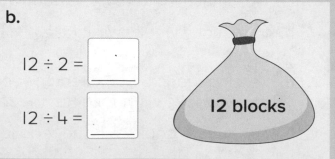

b.

12 ÷ 2 = ☐

12 ÷ 4 = ☐

12 blocks

2. Complete the multiplication fact you would use to figure out the division fact. Then complete the division fact.

a.

10 dots in total

$5 \times \underline{\hspace{1cm}} = 10$

$10 \div \underline{\hspace{1cm}} = 5$

b.

12 dots in total

$2 \times \underline{\hspace{1cm}} = 12$

$12 \div 2 = \underline{\hspace{1cm}}$

c.

40 dots in total

$4 \times \underline{\hspace{1cm}} = 40$

$40 \div \underline{\hspace{1cm}} = 4$

d.

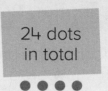

24 dots in total

$\underline{\hspace{1cm}} \times 4 = 24$

$24 \div \underline{\hspace{1cm}} = 4$

e.

8 dots in total

$\underline{\hspace{1cm}} \times 4 = 8$

$8 \div \underline{\hspace{1cm}} = \underline{\hspace{1cm}}$

f.

36 dots in total

$\underline{\hspace{1cm}} \times 9 = 36$

$36 \div \underline{\hspace{1cm}} = \underline{\hspace{1cm}}$

g.

18 dots in total

$2 \times \underline{\hspace{1cm}} = 18$

$18 \div \underline{\hspace{1cm}} = \underline{\hspace{1cm}}$

h.

14 dots in total

$\underline{\hspace{1cm}} \times 2 = 14$

$14 \div \underline{\hspace{1cm}} = \underline{\hspace{1cm}}$

3. Write a multiplication fact and division fact to match each problem. Use a **?** to show the unknown amount.

a.

Students are standing in two equal rows.

If there are 14 students in total, how many are in each row?

b.

32 chicken nuggets are shared equally among 8 friends.

How many nuggets are in each share?

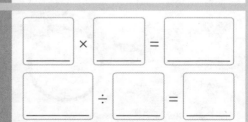

Step Ahead

Mr. Reed's class is planning a field trip. There are 22 students in the class. How many cars will be needed if 4 passengers fit in each car?

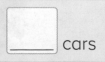

_____ cars

Computation Practice

★ Calculate the product for each. Use a green pencil to shade the circles that show products that have a 0 in the ones place.

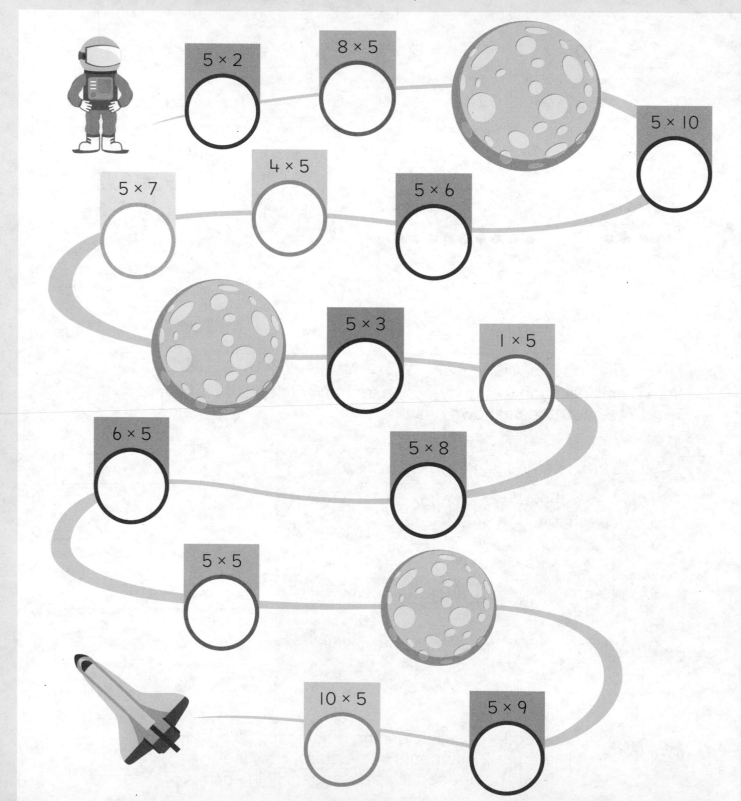

5 × 2

8 × 5

5 × 10

4 × 5

5 × 7

5 × 6

5 × 3

1 × 5

6 × 5

5 × 8

5 × 5

10 × 5

5 × 9

Ongoing Practice

1. Solve each problem. Show your thinking.

a. The nature club planted 395 birch trees and 274 pine trees. How many trees did they plant in total?

_____ trees

b. Noah collected 89 cans. Pamela collected 155 more cans than Noah. How many cans do they have in total?

_____ cans

2. Write the missing numbers to complete each fact family.

a.

$$6 \times 5 = 30$$

$$5 \times 6 = \boxed{}$$

$$\boxed{} \div 6 = 5$$

$$30 \div \boxed{} = 6$$

b.

$$\boxed{} \times 10 = 40$$

$$10 \times 4 = \boxed{}$$

$$40 \div \boxed{} = 10$$

$$40 \div 10 = \boxed{}$$

Preparing for Module 5

Draw jumps to show how you subtract. Then write the difference.

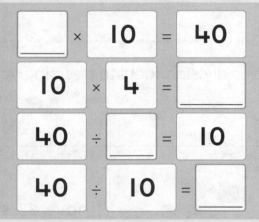

a.

$$164 - 7 = \boxed{}$$

b.

$$132 - 6 = \boxed{}$$

Step In

I have 20 seedlings to plant in my vegetable garden. How can I arrange them in equal rows?

How can you figure out the different arrangements that could be used?

Draw one arrangement. Write two multiplication facts to describe your array.

Write two division facts to describe your picture.

I have 32 seedlings to plant in my flower garden. How can I arrange them in equal rows?

Draw two **different** arrangements that could be made. Then write the multiplication facts and related division facts for each arrangement.

1. Color an array to match the numbers given.
   Then complete the fact family to match.

a.

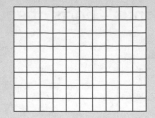

$4 \times 3 =$ _____

_____ $\times$ _____ $=$ _____

_____ $\div$ _____ $=$ _____

_____ $\div$ _____ $=$ _____

b.

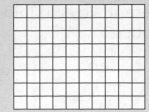

$2 \times 9 =$ _____

_____ $\times$ _____ $=$ _____

_____ $\div$ _____ $=$ _____

_____ $\div$ _____ $=$ _____

c.

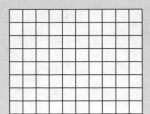

$2 \times 7 =$ _____

_____ $\times$ _____ $=$ _____

_____ $\div$ _____ $=$ _____

_____ $\div$ _____ $=$ _____

2. Complete each equation. Then use the same color to show the number facts that belong in the same fact family.

$16 \div \boxed{} = 2$ $16 \div 4 = \boxed{}$ $8 \times 2 = \boxed{}$ $\boxed{} = 24 \div 6$

$6 \times 4 = \boxed{}$ $3 \times \boxed{} = 12$ $\boxed{} = 4 \times 4$ $2 \times 8 = \boxed{}$

$\boxed{} = 12 \div 3$ $24 = 4 \times \boxed{}$ $12 \div 4 = \boxed{}$ $24 \div \boxed{} = 4$

Write the missing number to complete each fact.

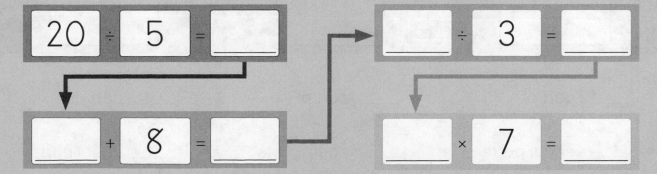

$20 \div 5 =$ _____   _____ $\div 3 =$ _____

_____ $+ 8 =$ _____   _____ $\times 7 =$ _____

Step In

These are three different ways to fold a square into 4 parts of equal size. What do you notice?

 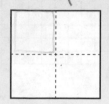 

Color one part of each large square. What fraction of each square did you color?

All the large squares are the same size and shape but they are split up in different ways.

How could you check that the shaded fraction of each square covers the same amount of paper?

> Each large square is called **one whole**.

Step Up

1. Each large square is one whole. Color one part of each. Then write how much is shaded and how many parts in total.

a.

| 1 | part of |
| 4 | equal parts |

b.

| 1 | part of |
| 2 | equal parts |

c.

| ___ | part of |
| ___ | equal parts |

d.

| ___ | part of |
| ___ | equal parts |

e.

| ___ | part of |
| ___ | equal parts |

f.

| ___ | part of |
| ___ | equal parts |

2. Each strip is one whole. Color one part of each.
Then write how much is shaded and how many parts there are in total.

a.

_1_ part of

_3_ equal parts

b.

_1_ part of

_2_ equal parts

c.

_1_ part of

_8_ equal parts

3. Each shape below is one whole. Color one part of each shape. Record the number of parts and then complete the fraction words.

a. _1_ part of _2_ equal parts _____ two _____ is shaded

b. _____ part of _____ equal parts _____ is shaded

c. _____ part of _____ equal parts _____ is shaded

Step Ahead

Ryan, Abey, and Max cut up a piece of paper and each took one-fourth of the paper.

Was the whole piece of paper used? How do you know?

Think and Solve Janice bought 2 different items. She spent $8.
Victor bought 3 different items. He spent $12.

Pen $4

Notebook $2

Marker $5

Sharpener $3

a. There are 2 items that they both bought. What are they?

b. Which item did neither of them buy?

Words at Work Write about two different strategies you could use to solve this equation. Be sure to include the answer.

$$36 \div 4 = ?$$

I. Write the difference. Draw jumps on the number line to show your thinking.

a.

652 − 41 = ☐

FROM 2.10.4

←――――――――――――――――――――――――――――――→

b.

375 − 52 = ☐

←――――――――――――――――――――――――――――――→

2. Write a multiplication fact and division fact to match each problem. Use a **?** to show the unknown amount.

FROM 3.4.4

a. Each roller coaster car carries 4 people. There are 20 people waiting in line. How many cars will be needed?

____ × ____ = _____

____ ÷ ____ = ____

b. 40 crates of oranges are shared equally among 5 stores. How many crates will each store receive?

____ × ____ = _____

____ ÷ ____ = ____

Preparing for Module 5

Use the count-back strategy to figure out the difference between the amount in the wallet and the price. Draw jumps on the number line to show your thinking.

a.

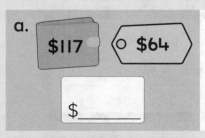

$ _____

←――――――――――――――――――――――――――――――→

b.

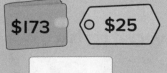

$ _____

←――――――――――――――――――――――――――――――→

Step In Layla is covering a rectangle with orange pattern blocks.

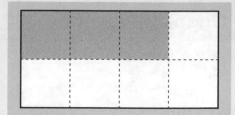

What fraction of the rectangle has she covered so far?

Write a numeral to show the number of parts that are covered and a numeral to show the number of equal parts in the whole.

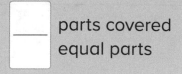

parts covered
equal parts

The numeral on the top is called the **numerator**.

The numeral on the bottom is called the **denominator**.

Together the two numerals make a **common fraction**.

In this picture, the numerator tells how many blocks have been used. The denominator tells how many blocks will cover the rectangle. Together they show that $\frac{3}{8}$ of the rectangle is covered.

Step Up 1. These fraction cards are sorted into rows. Complete the cards to match.

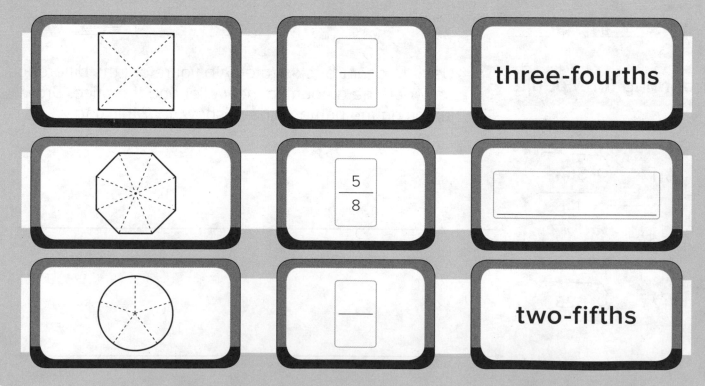

© ORIGO Education

2. Each large rectangle is one whole. Shade the fraction of each rectangle. Then write the fraction of the rectangle that is **not** shaded.

a.
$\frac{3}{8}$

b.
$\frac{2}{6}$

c.
$\frac{2}{3}$

d.
$\frac{4}{8}$

3. Each strip is one whole. Write the fraction that is shaded. Then write the fraction that is not shaded in words.

a.

b.

c.

Step Ahead

These fraction cards were sorted into one group. Color the card that does not belong.

$\frac{3}{8}$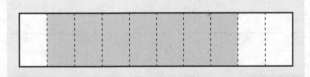

$\frac{7}{8}$

eight-tenths

$\frac{8}{8}$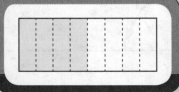

Step In   Fractions can also be shown on a number line.

On this number line the distance between 0 and I represents one whole.

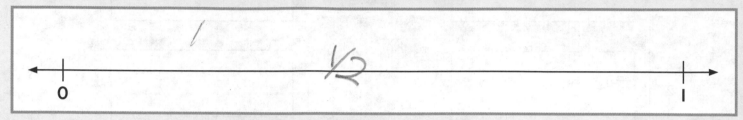

How can you find one-half on this number line?

Draw an ⌒→ from 0 to show one-half.

> The point that is halfway between 0 and I represents one-half.

What fraction is shown by the arrow on the number line below? How do you know?

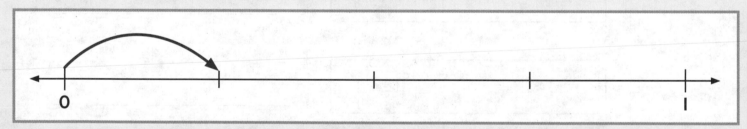

Step Up   I. The distance between 0 and I is one whole. Write the fraction shown by each arrow.

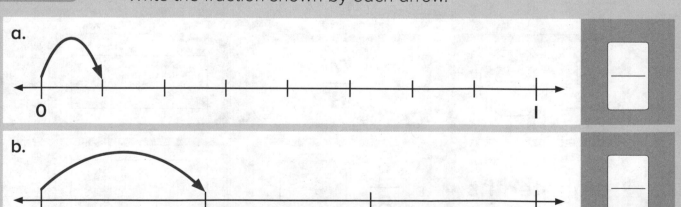

a.

b.

2. The distance between 0 and 1 is one whole. Split each number line into more equal parts. Then draw an arrow to show the fraction.

a.

one-fourth

b.

one-sixth

c.

one-eighth

3. Use the number lines on these pages. Color the ⬭ beside the fraction that is shorter.

a.
⬭ one-half

or

⬭ one-fourth

b.
⬭ one-third

or

⬭ one-sixth

c.
⬭ one-eighth

or

⬭ one-sixth

d.
⬭ one-third

or

⬭ one-half

e.
⬭ one-sixth

or

⬭ one-fourth

f.
⬭ one-half

or

⬭ one-sixth

Step Ahead

Two friends each buy a rope. The ropes are the same length. Cody cuts his rope into fourths. Nancy cuts her rope into thirds.

Who cuts the rope into more pieces? _____

Who cuts the rope into longer pieces? _____

Computation Practice

★ Complete the equations. Then write each letter above its matching product in the grid. Some letters appear more than once.

5 × 5 = _____ **l**

2 × 2 = _____ **m**

2 × 9 = _____ **t**

8 × 5 = _____ **n**

3 × 2 = _____ **a**

8 × 2 = _____ **e**

7 × 5 = _____ **q**

5 × 9 = _____ **y**

2 × 0 = _____ **i**

1 × 5 = _____ **s**

5 × 2 = _____ **u**

4 × 5 = _____ **o**

6 × 5 = _____ **f**

2 × 6 = _____ **b**

_____	_____	_____	_____	_____	_____	_____	_____	_____	_____
20	40	25	45	30	16	4	6	25	16

_____	_____	_____	_____	_____	_____	_____	_____	_____	_____
4	20	5	35	10	0	18	20	16	5

_____	_____	_____	_____
12	0	18	16

Complete these facts as fast as you can.

3 × 4 = _____

4 × 1 = _____

4 × 6 = _____

4 × 7 = _____

9 × 4 = _____

4 × 8 = _____

4 × 5 = _____

2 × 4 = _____

4 × 4 = _____

Ongoing Practice

1. Split each number into hundreds, tens, and ones.
There is more than one way.

a. 375

is equal to

_____ hundreds, _____ tens, and _____ ones

b. 215

is equal to

_____ hundreds, _____ tens, and _____ ones

c. 836

is equal to

_____ hundreds, _____ tens, and _____ ones

d. 409

is equal to

_____ hundreds, _____ tens, and _____ ones

2. Each large rectangle is one whole. Shade the fraction of each rectangle.
Then write the fraction of the rectangle that is **not** shaded.

a. $\dfrac{1}{4}$ _____

b. $\dfrac{4}{6}$ _____

c. $\dfrac{2}{5}$ _____

d. $\dfrac{3}{8}$ _____

Preparing for Module 5

Draw jumps to show how you could **count on** to find the difference. Then write the difference.

a.
$56 - 37 = \boxed{}$

b.
$61 - 48 = \boxed{}$

Step In

Look at this number line.

The distance from 0 to 1 is one whole.

Show how you would mark $\frac{1}{6}$ on the number line.

> I would split the line from 0 to 1 into 6 equal parts. The distance from 0 to the first mark will be $\frac{1}{6}$ of the total distance from 0 to 1.

Charlie is making a cake.

$\frac{1}{4}$ cup

He needs $\frac{3}{4}$ cup of sugar but only has a $\frac{1}{4}$ measuring cup.

What can he do to measure the correct amount of sugar?

What does this number line show?

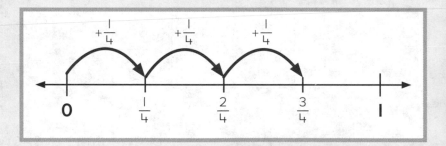

Step Up

1. Look at how each number line has been split up. The distance from 0 to 1 is one whole. Write the fraction that each arrow is pointing to.

a.

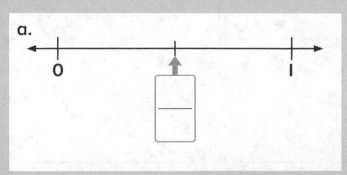

b.

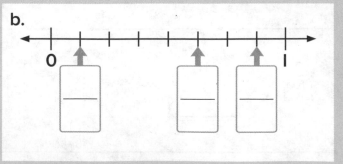

2. For each number line, the distance from 0 to 1 is one whole. Write the answer to each problem. Draw jumps on the number line to show your thinking.

a. Teresa has a bottle that holds $\frac{1}{6}$ of a gallon of water. How many bottles will she need to make $\frac{4}{6}$ of a gallon of water?

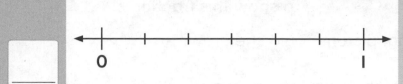

b. John's family bought a pizza cut into eighths. John ate $\frac{3}{8}$ of the whole pizza. How many pieces of pizza did he eat?

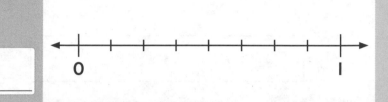

3. Write an addition equation to match the jumps on the number line.

a.

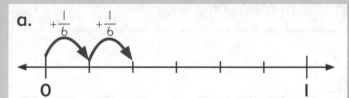

$= \dfrac{}{}$

b.

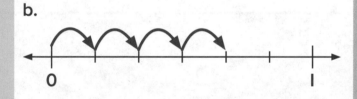

$= \dfrac{}{}$

c.

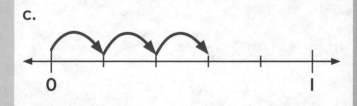

$= \dfrac{}{}$

Step Ahead   Complete each equation.

a. $\dfrac{1}{3} + \dfrac{1}{3} + \dfrac{1}{3} = \dfrac{}{3}$

b. $\dfrac{1}{8} + \dfrac{1}{8} + \dfrac{1}{8} + \dfrac{1}{8} + \dfrac{1}{8} = \dfrac{}{8}$

c. $\dfrac{1}{2} + \dfrac{1}{2} = \dfrac{}{2}$

Step In

Mako is asked to draw a picture to show this fraction.

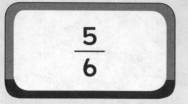

$$\frac{5}{6}$$

What picture could she draw?

How could you show $\frac{5}{6}$ using each of these models?

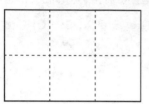

Draw an arrow to show the same fraction on this number line.

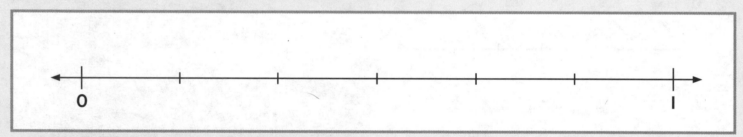

How did you decide where to draw the arrow?

Step Up

1. Show the same fraction on each model.

a.

$$\frac{3}{5}$$

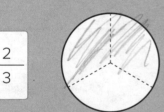

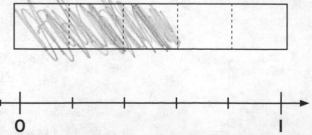

b.

$$\frac{2}{3}$$

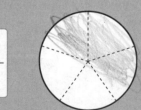

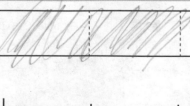

2. Write the fraction that is shown on each model.

a.

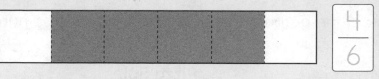

$\dfrac{4}{6}$

b.

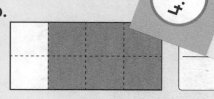

c.

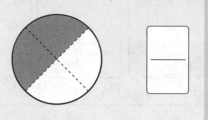

d.

e.

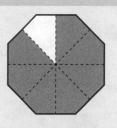

f.

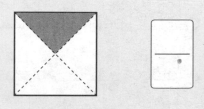

g.

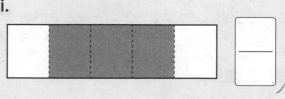

h.

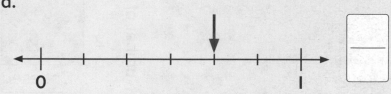

i.

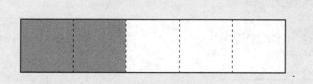

j.

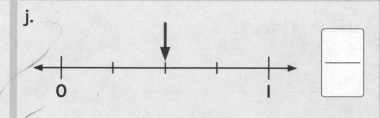

Step Ahead

List the fractions from Question 2 that you think are **greater than one-half**.

Think and Solve

Look at the graph and clues. Write the missing numbers.

Clues

- Half as many veggie as cheese pizzas were sold.
- Twice as many pepperoni as sausage pizzas were sold.

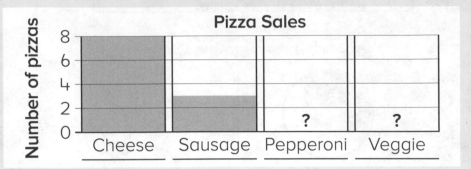

Pizza Sales

a. _____ pepperoni pizzas and _____ veggie pizzas were sold.

b. A total of _____ pizzas were sold.

Words at Work

These three models show the same fraction.

Number line model	Area model	Length model
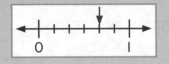		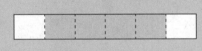

Write the fraction that is shown. Then write how the models are the same and different.

I. Draw jumps to show how you subtract.
Then write the differences.

a.

$475 - 127 =$ ____

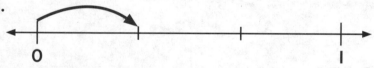

b.

$651 - 135 =$ ____

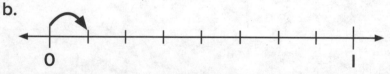

2. The distance between 0 and 1 is one whole. Write the fraction shown by each jump.
Then write the fraction in words.

a.

b.

Preparing for Module 5

Draw jumps on the number line to calculate
the difference. Make the first jump to 100.

a.

$116 - 87 =$ ____

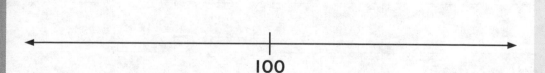

100

b.

$125 - 79 =$ ____

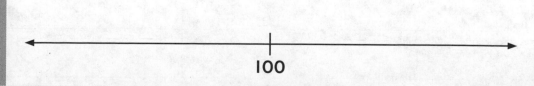

100

FROM 2.10.10

FROM 3.4.10

Step In

Look at this array. What do you see?

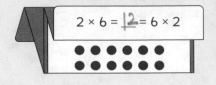

$2 \times 6 = 12 = 6 \times 2$

What strategy can you use to figure out the product?

Look at the next array. What do you see?

What strategy can you use to figure out the product?

I used the double-double strategy.

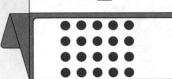

$2 \times 6 = \underline{} = 6 \times 2$

$4 \times 6 = \underline{} = 6 \times 4$

Look at the next array. What do you see?

How can you use the fours fact to help you figure out the product for the eights fact?

8 sixes is the same as double double double 6.

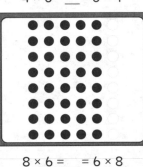

$2 \times 6 = \underline{} = 6 \times 2$

$4 \times 6 = \underline{} = 6 \times 4$

$8 \times 6 = \underline{} = 6 \times 8$

Is this an easy strategy to use?

What other eights facts could you solve using this strategy?

Step Up

I. Look at these pictures. Write the products.

a.

double 9

$2 \times 9 = \boxed{18}$

b.

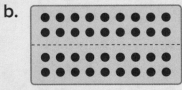

double double 9

$4 \times 9 = \boxed{36}$

c.

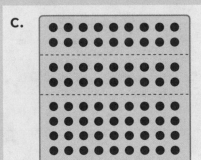

double double double 9

$8 \times 9 = \boxed{72}$

© ORIGO Education

2. Write the products for these.

a.

$2 \times 3 =$ 6
$4 \times 3 =$ 12
$8 \times 3 =$ 24

b.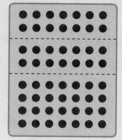

$2 \times 7 =$ 14
$4 \times 7 =$ 28
$8 \times 7 =$ 52

c.

$2 \times 5 =$ 10
$4 \times 5 =$ 20
$8 \times 5 =$ 40

d.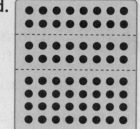

$2 \times 8 =$ 16
$4 \times 8 =$ 32
$8 \times 8 =$ 64

3. Use a doubling strategy to complete this table.

Number	Double (×2)	Double Double (×4)	Double Double Double (×8)
6	12	24	48
7	14	28	46
10	20	40	80
		36	

Step Ahead

Write numbers in the squares so that the numbers in each row and column multiply to give the product in the circle.

a.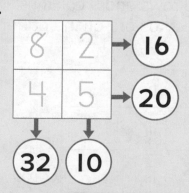

| 8 | 2 | → 16 |
| 4 | 5 | → 20 |

↓ 32 ↓ 10

b.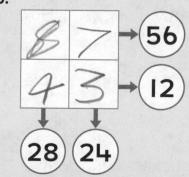

| 8 | 7 | → 56 |
| 4 | 3 | → 12 |

↓ 28 ↓ 24

c.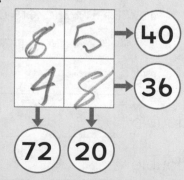

| 8 | 5 | → 40 |
| 4 | 8 | → 36 |

↓ 72 ↓ 20

Step In   Thomas bought **8** of these packs of pencils.

How many pencils did he buy in total?

How could you figure it out?

Write the numbers needed in each of the boxes below
to show how many pencils he bought.

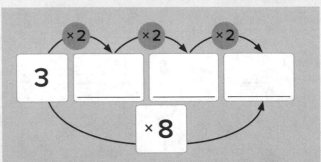

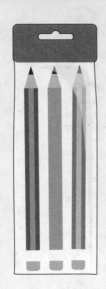

Double 3 is 6, double 6
is 12, and double 12 is 24.
So 8 packs of 3 is 24.

**Leila bought 8 different packs of pencils.
Each pack had 2 pencils. How many pencils did she buy?**

How could you figure it out?

It is easier to think double 8 than double double double 2.

What other problems could you solve using these strategies?

Step Up   **1.** Show how you could use the **double-double-double strategy**
to solve each problem.

a. Aaron bought 8 packs of stickers.
There are 6 stickers in each pack.
How many stickers did he buy
in total?

double _____ is _____

double _____ is _____

double _____ is _____ stickers

b. Trading cards are displayed on
a page in 8 rows and 9 columns.
How many cards are on the page?

double _____ is _____

double _____ is _____

double _____ is _____ cards

2. Write the missing numbers.

a.
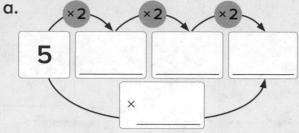

b.
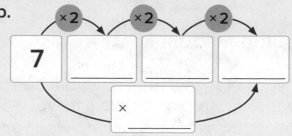

c.
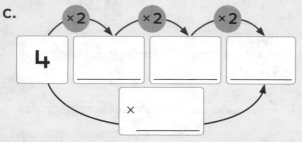

d.
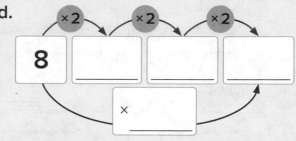

3. Complete each fact. Then write the turnaround fact for each.

a.

$8 \times 3 = $ _____

_____ $\times$ _____ $=$ _____

b.

$8 \times 6 = $ _____

_____ $\times$ _____ $=$ _____

c.

$8 \times 2 = $ _____

_____ $\times$ _____ $=$ _____

4. Think about the fours and eights facts. Write the missing number in each equation.

a.
$4 \times 7 = \boxed{}$

b.
$16 = 2 \times \boxed{}$

c.
$\boxed{} \times 4 = 36$

d.
$24 = \boxed{} \times 6$

e.
$\boxed{} \times 8 = 64$

f.
$40 = \boxed{} \times 10$

g.
$7 \times \boxed{} = 56$

h.
$32 = \boxed{} \times 8$

i.
$3 \times 8 = \boxed{}$

Step Ahead

Use repeated doubling to complete the missing numbers.

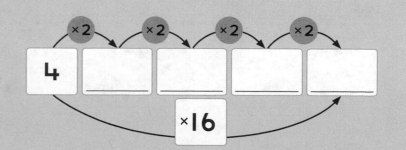

Computation Practice

★ For each of these, write the product. Then write the turnaround fact. Use the classroom clock to time yourself.

Time Taken:

start | $5 \times 6 =$ ☐ = ☐ × ☐ | $4 \times 2 =$ ☐ = ☐ × ☐

$5 \times 7 =$ ☐ = ☐ × ☐ | $4 \times 5 =$ ☐ = ☐ × ☐

$9 \times 2 =$ ☐ = ☐ × ☐ | $2 \times 5 =$ ☐ = ☐ × ☐

$2 \times 3 =$ ☐ = ☐ × ☐ | $9 \times 5 =$ ☐ = ☐ × ☐

$5 \times 8 =$ ☐ = ☐ × ☐ | $0 \times 5 =$ ☐ = ☐ × ☐

$6 \times 2 =$ ☐ = ☐ × ☐ | $2 \times 1 =$ ☐ = ☐ × ☐

$3 \times 5 =$ ☐ = ☐ × ☐ | $0 \times 2 =$ ☐ = ☐ × ☐

finish | $5 \times 1 =$ ☐ = ☐ × ☐ | $8 \times 2 =$ ☐ = ☐ × ☐

Complete these facts as fast as you can.

$5 \times 5 =$ _____ $2 \times 6 =$ _____ $8 \times 5 =$ _____

$2 \times 8 =$ _____ $6 \times 5 =$ _____ $5 \times 9 =$ _____

$5 \times 7 =$ _____ $4 \times 2 =$ _____ $2 \times 2 =$ _____

Ongoing Practice

1. Write **is greater than** or **is less than** to make each statement true.

a.
1,149 _____ 1,094

b.
989 _____ 998

c.
1,012 _____ 1,021

d.
1,191 _____ 1,094

2. Write the products.

a.
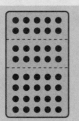

2 × 5 = _____

4 × 5 = _____

8 × 5 = _____

b.
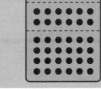

2 × 6 = _____

4 × 6 = _____

8 × 6 = _____

c.

2 × 3 = _____

4 × 3 = _____

8 × 3 = _____

d.
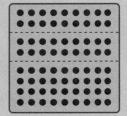

2 × 9 = _____

4 × 9 = _____

8 × 9 = _____

Preparing for Module 6   Complete these equations.

a.
10 × _____ = 40

b.
_____ × 1 = 10

c.
10 × _____ = 70

d.
8 × _____ = 80

e.
10 × 3 = _____

f.
_____ × 10 = 90

g.
_____ × 10 = 20

h.
10 × 7 = _____

i.
_____ × 5 = 50

Step In Look at this hundred chart.

1	2	3	4	5	6	7	8	9	10
11	12	13	14	15	16	17	18	19	20
21	22	23	24	25	26	27	28	29	30
31	32	33	34	35	36	37	38	39	40
41	42	43	44	45	46	47	48	49	50
51	52	53	54	55	56	57	58	59	60
61	62	63	64	65	66	67	68	69	70
71	72	73	74	75	76	77	78	79	80
81	82	83	84	85	86	87	88	89	90
91	92	93	94	95	96	97	98	99	100

Use red to color all the numbers above that you
know are products of the eights facts.

There are two numbers in the bottom two rows that
are the products of 8 × 11 and 8 × 12.

Is there a pattern you can see that could help you
figure out the numbers?

What strategy could you
use to check your answer?

Imagine the chart continued to 200.
What are some other numbers you would color to continue the pattern?

How do you know?

1. Look at the color pattern of numbers. Are the numbers odd or even? _____

2. Look at the red numbers in a single column. What do you notice?

3. Look at the numbers that lie along a sloping line. What change happens in the ones digit from one number to the next?

4. a. Circle all the numbers in the chart that are products of the fours facts.

   b. What pattern do you notice?

Step Ahead   Complete these facts. Then write about the pattern you notice.

$8 \times \boxed{} = 32$

$4 \times \boxed{} = 32$

$2 \times \boxed{} = 32$

Step In   What do you see in this picture?

What equation could you write to describe the row of vehicles?

What else might you see in one row? Draw a picture to match.

Write an equation to describe your picture.

Step Up   I. Complete the picture to match the problem.
Then complete the multiplication fact to match.

a. **7 birds sitting on a fence**
How many birds in total?

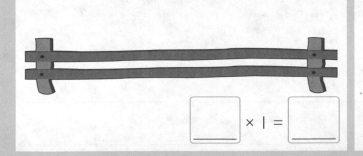

____ × I = ____

b. **6 cookies in a jar**
How many cookies in total?

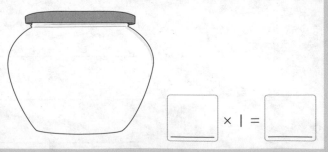

____ × I = ____

2. Complete the multiplication fact to match each picture.

a. One ball for each student	**b.** One line of ducks
How many balls in total?	How many ducks in total?

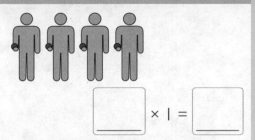

[ ] × 1 = [ ]

[ ] × 1 = [ ]

3. For each of these, write a number greater than one but less than 10.
Then draw a matching picture and write the related multiplication fact.

a. [ ] bananas in a bunch

[ ] × [ ] = [ ]

b. [ ] stamps in a row

[ ] × [ ] = [ ]

c. [ ] muffins on a tray

[ ] × [ ] = [ ]

d. [ ] flowers in a vase

[ ] × [ ] = [ ]

Step Ahead Write a rule you can use when you multiply by one.

_____

_____

Think and Solve

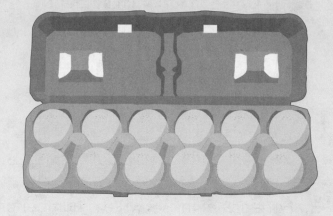

3 eggs make 5 omelets.

6 eggs make 10 omelets.

9 eggs make 15 omelets.

Complete these sentences.

a. 12 eggs make _____ omelets.

b. _____ eggs make 35 omelets.

Words at Work Write about how the twos, fours, and eights multiplication facts are related.

_____

_____

_____

_____

_____

_____

_____

_____

_____

I. Round each number to the nearest ten.

a. 753 _____

b. 478 _____

c. 398 _____

d. 3,616 _____

e. 7,854 _____

f. 5,405 _____

2. Complete each picture.

a.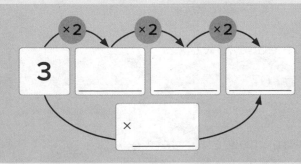

b.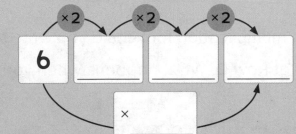

c.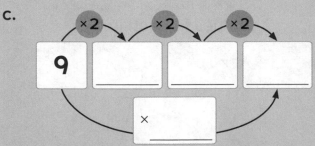

d.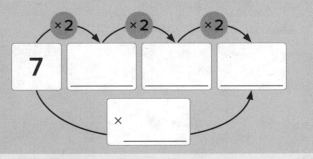

Preparing for Module 6

Look at the prices on the menu. Write equations to figure out these problems.

a. What is the total cost of 5 sandwiches?

_____

b. What is the total cost of 8 drinks?

_____

c. What is the total cost of 9 meal deals?

_____

MENU

Sandwich	$3
Drink	$2
Meal deal	$4

Step In   Describe what you see in each row.

Row A

Row B

Row C

Row D

What multiplication fact could you write to describe each row?

Look at Row D. What happens when you multiply by 0?

Step Up   I.   Draw the picture. Then write the multiplication fact.

a.   **3 cookies in each jar**

3 × ☐ = ☐

b.   **2 cookies in each jar**

3 × ☐ = ☐

c.   **I cookie in each jar**

3 × ☐ = ☐

d.   **0 cookies in each jar**

3 × ☐ = ☐

2. Draw rows of 5 stars on the flag to match each multiplication fact.

a.

$3 \times 5 = 15$

b.
$2 \times 5 = 10$

c.

$1 \times 5 = 5$

d.
$0 \times 5 = 0$

3. Draw jumps on the number line to show each fact. Then write the products.

a.

$4 \times 2 = \boxed{}$

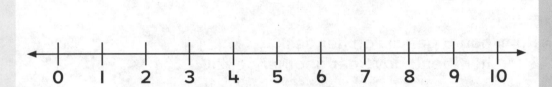

b.

$4 \times 1 = \boxed{}$

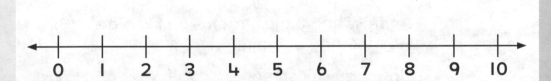

c.

$4 \times 0 = \boxed{}$

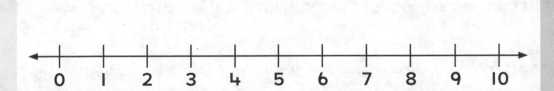

Step Ahead   Write a rule you can use when you multiply by 0.

Step In   Damon planted seedlings in one row of 6.

How many seedlings did he plant? How do you know?

Mia had **6** packets of stickers. She gave stickers to each of her friends until the packets were empty.

How many stickers did Mia have left? How do you know?

Ruby had **6** pencils on her desk.
Then her friend gave her another pencil.

How many pencils did Ruby have in total? How do you know?

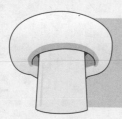

Andrew had **6** mushrooms on his plate.
He ate none of them.

How many mushrooms did Andrew eat? How do you know?

What can you say about the math involved in each story?

Step Up   I.   Read the equation carefully. Then write the answer.

a. $5 \times 1 =$ _____

b. $9 \times 1 =$ _____

c. $8 \times 0 =$ _____

d. $1 \times 7 =$ _____

e. $0 \times 4 =$ _____

f. $5 \times 1 =$ _____

g. $37 \times 1 =$ _____

h. $97 \times 0 =$ _____

i. $0 \times 58 =$ _____

2. Multiply the two numbers across each row and write the product in the matching circle. Then multiply the two numbers down each column and write the product in the matching circle.

a.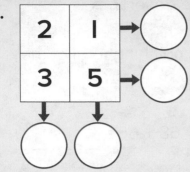

b.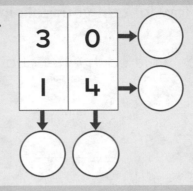

c.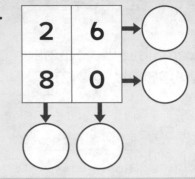

3. Figure out what numbers must be in each row and column to make the product in the matching circle.

a.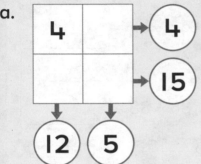

b.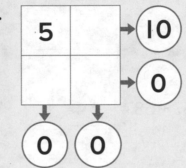

c.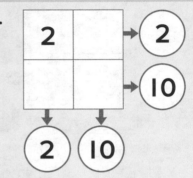

d.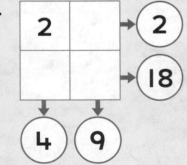

e.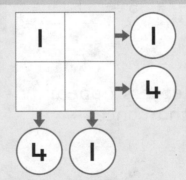

f.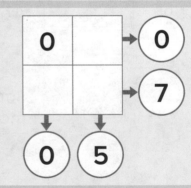

Step Ahead Write a story problem to match this fact. $1 \times 9 = 9$

How far can you walk into the desert?

★ Complete the equations. Then write each letter above its matching total at the bottom of the page.

55 + 56 = _____	**t**
98 + 97 = _____	**y**
87 + 88 = _____	**o**
75 + 76 = _____	**f**
66 + 65 = _____	**u**

87 + 86 = _____	**e**
76 + 77 = _____	**a**
67 + 65 = _____	**r**
57 + 58 = _____	**g**
97 + 95 = _____	**h**

68 + 66 = _____	**i**
58 + 56 = _____	**l**
95 + 96 = _____	**n**
86 + 88 = _____	**k**
77 + 78 = _____	**w**

Some letters appear more than once.

| 192 | 153 | 114 | 151 | 155 | 153 | 195 | – | 153 | 151 | 111 | 173 | 132 |

| 111 | 192 | 153 | 111 | | 195 | 175 | 131 | | 153 | 132 | 173 |

| 155 | 153 | 114 | 174 | 134 | 191 | 115 | | 175 | 131 | 111 |

Ongoing Practice

1. Complete these facts.

a.

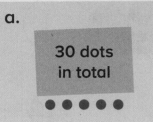

30 dots in total

_____ × 5 = 30

30 ÷ 5 = _____

b.

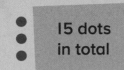

15 dots in total

3 × _____ = 15

15 ÷ 3 = _____

c.

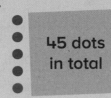

45 dots in total

5 × _____ = 45

45 ÷ 5 = _____

d.

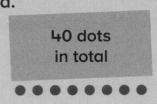

40 dots in total

_____ × 8 = 40

40 ÷ 8 = _____

2. a. Draw jumps on the number line to show each equation. Then write the products.

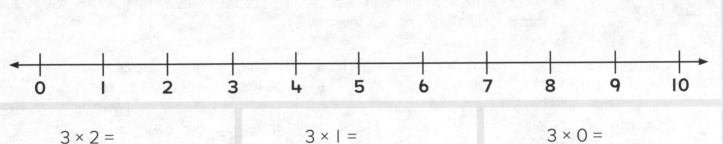

3 × 2 = _____

3 × 1 = _____

3 × 0 = _____

b. What happens when you multiply by 0?

Preparing for Module 6

Use a **doubling strategy** to complete this table.

	Number	Double (×2)	Double Double (×4)	Double Double Double (×8)
a.	9	18		
b.	4			
c.	7			

Step In   There are **6 plates** on a picnic table.

Each plate has **4 strawberries**.

There is also one banana on **2 of the plates**.

How many strawberries are there in total?
How do you know?

What numbers in the story helped you?

Which numbers would you use to figure out how many pieces of fruit there are in total?

There are 6 plates with 4 strawberries on each plate.

Step Up   **I.** Write an equation to match each problem. Use a **?** for the unknown amount. Then calculate the answer.

a. A teacher has 5 rulers. Each ruler is one foot long and 3 of them are plastic. What is the total length of the rulers if they are laid end to end?

☐ × ☐ = ☐

☐ feet

b. Every day Laura and 2 of her friends jog 3 laps around the athletics track. How many laps will Laura jog in 8 days?

☐ × ☐ = ☐

☐ laps

c. Nathan arranges a bookcase so that each shelf has 9 books. There are 4 shelves of books. 7 of the books are about cats. How many books are there in total?

☐ × ☐ = ☐

☐ books

d. Chairs in an auditorium are set out in 6 rows. There are 8 chairs in each row. Only 5 people sit in each row. How many people are there in total?

☐ × ☐ = ☐

☐ people

2. Write an equation to match each problem. Use a **?** for the unknown amount. Then calculate the answer.

a. Rozene has 4 pieces of ribbon. Each ribbon is 3 feet long. She needs twice the total length that she has. How many feet of ribbon does Rozene need in total?

_____ feet

b. A fruit store sells 3-kilogram bags of apples and oranges. Dad buys 2 bags of oranges and 6 bags of apples. What is the total mass of all the fruit dad buys?

_____ kg

c. Oscar bakes a tray of cookies. The tray holds 4 rows of cookies with 7 cookies in each row. He has some cookie dough left over so he bakes another tray that has only one row of 7 cookies on it. How many cookies does he bake?

_____ cookies

Step Ahead

Write a word problem that matches this calculation.

4 × 6, then add 3

_____

_____

_____

Step In   Imagine you have $55 in your wallet.

TICKETS

Child $16
Adult $24

How much money will you have left if you buy one child ticket?

Nam used blocks to figure out the amount.

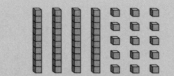

| First he showed 55. | Then he regrouped one tens block as 10 ones blocks. | Then he removed 16 to find the amount left over. |

Why did Nam regroup one of the tens blocks as 10 ones blocks?

What amount is left?

Carlos used a different strategy. He counted back by tens and then ones on a number line.

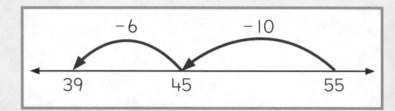

−6   −10

39   45   55

Which strategy do you like best? Why?

How much will you have left over if you buy one adult ticket?

Step Up   I. In each picture, a tens block has been regrouped as 10 ones blocks. Cross out blocks and complete sentences to calculate the difference.

a.
43 − 15 = ☐

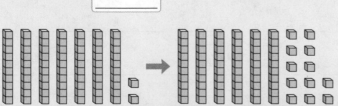

There are ☐ tens.

There are ☐ ones.

☐ and ☐ is ☐

b.
72 − 26 = ☐

There are ☐ tens.

There are ☐ ones.

☐ and ☐ is ☐

2. Use the count-back strategy to calculate each difference. Draw jumps on the number line to show your thinking.

a.

$56 - 18 =$ ⬚

⟵————————————————————⟶

b.

$84 - 26 =$ ⬚

⟵————————————————————⟶

c.

$105 - 17 =$ ⬚

⟵————————————————————⟶

3. Calculate the difference. Draw jumps on the number line to show your thinking.

a.

$145 - 28 =$ ⬚

⟵————————————————————⟶

b.

$113 - 35 =$ ⬚

⟵————————————————————⟶

Step Ahead

Imagine you use two $50 bills to buy tickets for 2 adults and one child. How much change will you get?

TICKETS

Child $18

Adult $27

$_____

Working Space

© ORIGO Education

Think and Solve Same shapes are the same price.
Write the cost of each shape.

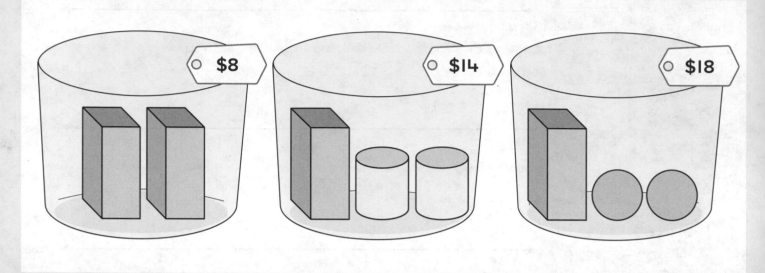

Words at Work Write a word problem that you could solve using the eights multiplication strategy. Then write how you find the solution.

1. Complete the multiplication fact you would use to figure out the division fact. Then complete the division fact.

FROM 3.4.6

a.

20 dots in total

● ● ● ● ●

$\boxed{}$ × 5 = 20

20 ÷ $\boxed{}$ = $\boxed{}$

b.

24 dots in total

● ● ● ● ● ●

$\boxed{}$ × 6 = 24

24 ÷ $\boxed{}$ = $\boxed{}$

c.

● 14 dots
● in total

2 × $\boxed{}$ = 14

14 ÷ $\boxed{}$ = $\boxed{}$

d.

16 dots in total

● ● ● ●

$\boxed{}$ × 4 = 16

16 ÷ $\boxed{}$ = $\boxed{}$

2. Write an equation to match. Use a **?** to show the unknown amount. Then write the answer.

FROM 3.5.7

a. Dad had 10 lengths of lumber. Each length was 6 feet long. He used 4 lengths. How many feet of lumber did he use?

$\boxed{}$ × $\boxed{}$ = $\boxed{}$

$\boxed{}$ feet

b. Shirts are $8 each and shorts are $10 each. How much will 3 shirts cost?

$\boxed{}$ × $\boxed{}$ = $\boxed{}$

$ $\boxed{}$

Complete the number fact to match each picture.

a. **1 line of 5 children**
How many children in total?

1 × $\boxed{}$ = $\boxed{}$

b. **1 flower in each vase**
How many flowers in total?

$\boxed{}$ × 1 = $\boxed{}$

© ORIGO Education

Step In

How could you figure out the amount of money left on the gift card after buying the skateboard?

$175
Gift Card

Nicole used a number line to figure it out.

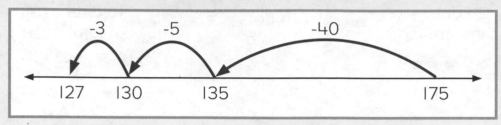

-3   -5   -40

127   130   135   175

How does she figure out the amount left on the gift card?

Dixon drew this picture to figure out the amount of money left on the gift card after buying the helmet.

$245
Gift Card

$109

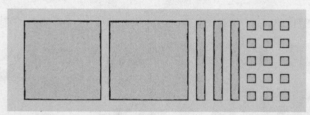

Why did he draw 3 tens blocks and 15 ones blocks?

How much money is left on the gift card?

Step Up

1. Calculate how much money is left on the gift card. Draw pictures to show your thinking.

a.

$165

$38

$ _____

b.

$145

$62

$ _____

2. Calculate the amount left on the gift card. Draw jumps on the number line to show your thinking.

a.

$27

$160

$ _____

b.

$58

$185

$ _____

c.

$129

$275

$ _____

3. Calculate each difference. You can use blocks or make notes on page 194 to help.

a.
129 – 45 = _____

b.
294 – 135 = _____

c.
305 – 121 = _____

Step Ahead

Stella had $125. She bought some of these items. She now has $46 left. Which items did she buy? She may have bought more than one of each item.

DVD Player $99

Headphones $40

DVDs $15 each

DVD Set $49

Step In

How many more points did the visiting team score than the home team?

Gavin used a count-on strategy to calculate the difference.

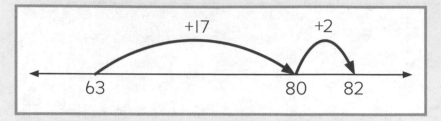

+17   +2

63   80   82

How would you calculate the difference?

Where is it located on the number line?

Counting on is a useful strategy when the difference is small.

Draw jumps on this number line to calculate the difference between these two scores.

Step Up

I. Count on from the lesser score to the greater score to calculate the difference. Draw jumps on the number line to show your thinking.

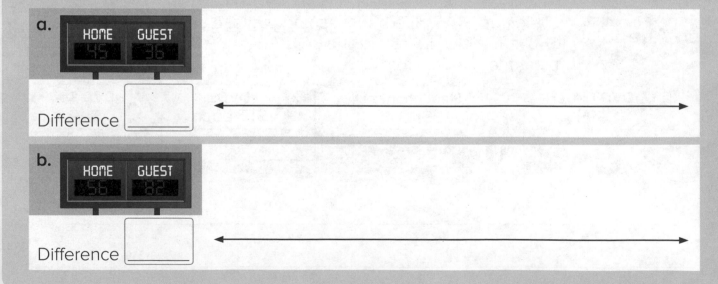

a.

HOME 45   GUEST 36

Difference ☐

b.

HOME 56   GUEST 82

Difference ☐

2. Use the count-on strategy to calculate the difference between these scores.

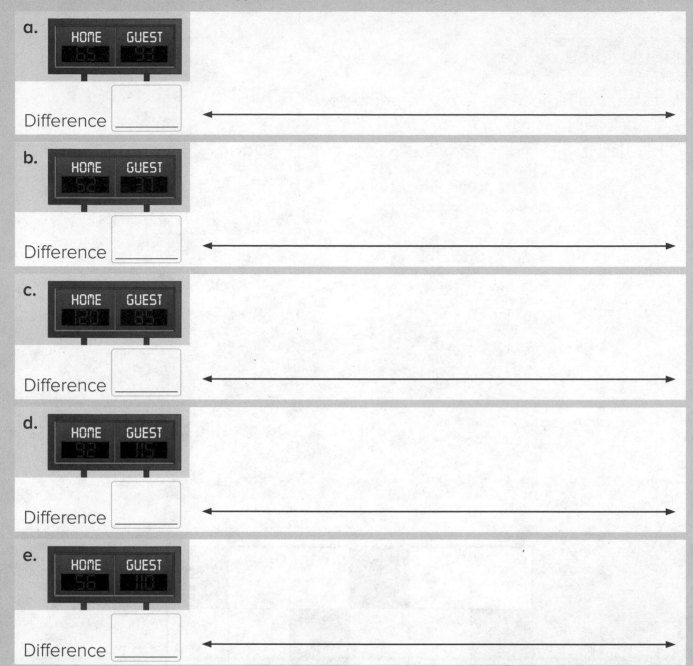

a.

HOME	GUEST
85	93

Difference _____ ←————————————————————————→

b.

HOME	GUEST
52	87

Difference _____ ←————————————————————————→

c.

HOME	GUEST
120	85

Difference _____ ←————————————————————————→

d.

HOME	GUEST
92	115

Difference _____ ←————————————————————————→

e.

HOME	GUEST
56	110

Difference _____ ←————————————————————————→

Step Ahead

Marcos's basketball team scored 81 points in total. They scored 15 points in the 4th period, 18 points in the 3rd period, and 20 points in the 2nd period.

How many points did they score in the 1st period?

_____ points

Computation Practice

★ Write each difference in the puzzle grid below.

Across	Down
a. 68 – 44	**b.** 77 – 34
c. 87 – 65	**d.** 46 – 23
e. 76 – 41	**f.** 85 – 34
g. 57 – 21	**h.** 97 – 34
j. 37 – 24	**i.** 78 – 54
l. 65 – 24	**k.** 69 – 36
n. 88 – 51	**m.** 98 – 81
p. 89 – 16	**o.** 95 – 23
r. 39 – 18	**q.** 49 – 11
t. 96 – 14	**s.** 58 – 42

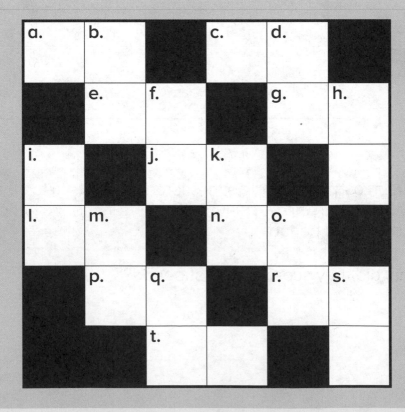

ORIGO Stepping Stones · Grade 3 · 5.10

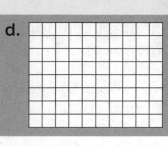
Ongoing Practice

1. Color an array to match the numbers given. Then complete the fact family to match.

a.
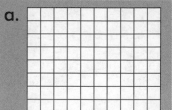

$4 \times 5 =$ _____

____ $\times$ ____ $=$ ____

____ $\div$ ____ $=$ ____

____ $\div$ ____ $=$ ____

b.
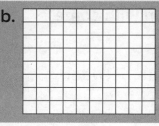

$8 \times 2 =$ _____

____ $\times$ ____ $=$ ____

____ $\div$ ____ $=$ ____

____ $\div$ ____ $=$ ____

c.
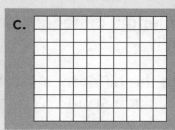

$5 \times 7 =$ _____

____ $\times$ ____ $=$ ____

____ $\div$ ____ $=$ ____

____ $\div$ ____ $=$ ____

d.
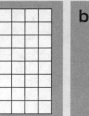

$4 \times 8 =$ _____

____ $\times$ ____ $=$ ____

____ $\div$ ____ $=$ ____

____ $\div$ ____ $=$ ____

2. In this picture a tens block has regrouped as 10 ones blocks.
Cross out blocks and complete sentences to figure out the difference.

$62 - 15 =$ ☐

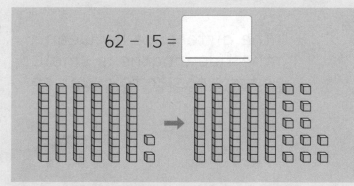

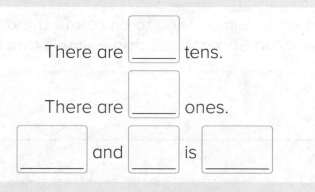

There are ☐ _____ tens.

There are ☐ _____ ones.

☐ _____ and ☐ _____ is ☐ _____

FROM 3.5.8

Preparing for Module 6

This table shows the number of cubes students can hold in one hand. Draw ☐ to show the data in the graph.

Student	
Daniela	卌 I
William	卌 卌
Kinu	卌 III

Cubes We Can Hold   ☐ means I cube

Student									
Daniela									
William									
Kinu									

Step In

Trina measures the length of her arm span.

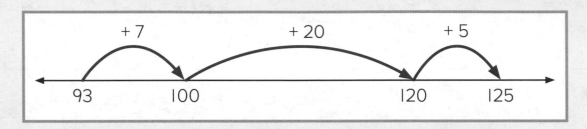

Trina	125 cm
David	93 cm
Samantha	167 cm
Felipe	182 cm

She then compares the length of her arm span with some other people in her family.

How could she calculate the difference in length between her arm span and David's arm span?

Trina uses a number line.

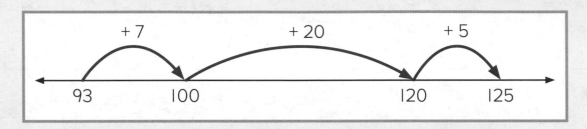

How does she calculate the difference? What steps does she follow?

Why did she decide to count on instead of count back?

Use this number line to calculate the difference between Samantha's and Felipe's arm spans.

The difference between the two lengths is small, so it's easier to count on.

Step Up

1. Calculate the difference between David's arm span and Samantha's arm span. Draw jumps on the number line to show your thinking.

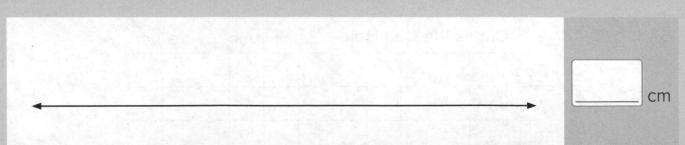

_____ cm

© ORIGO Education

2. Calculate each difference. Draw jumps on the number line to show your thinking.

a.

$130 - 83 = \boxed{}$

b.

$113 - 65 = \boxed{}$

c.

$172 - 108 = \boxed{}$

3. Calculate each difference. Show your thinking.

a.

$124 - 75 = \boxed{}$

b.

$342 - 195 = \boxed{}$

Step Ahead

Use the number line to help solve this problem. There is more than one possible answer.

Jamal and Allison have each saved more than $100. Allison has saved $45 more than Jamal. How much might each person have saved?

Jamal	Allison
$_____	$_____

Step In   Sofia wants to buy one of these guitars.

About how much will she save if she buys
the less expensive guitar?

$158

$95

Do you think she
will save more or
less than $50?

What method would you use to calculate the exact amount?

What steps would you take to solve this word problem?

Jude has $290 in his bank account. If he buys a scooter for $145 and a
helmet for $23, how much money will he have left in his bank account?

I'll call the total cost C.
C = 145 + 23
The amount Jude has left is $290 – C.

Step Up   I. Write equations to match each problem. Use a letter or other
symbol for the unknown amount. Then calculate the answer.

a. Pati has saved $170. She buys a coffee table for $87 and a chair for $50. How much money does she have left in her savings?	b. Paul buys 89 yards of wire fencing for a garden and a chicken coop. Afterward, he has 25 yards left. How many yards of fencing did he use?
$_____	_____ yd

2. Solve each problem. Show your thinking.

a. Archie walks 263 steps to school. Franco walks 148 steps to the same school. What is the difference between the number of steps?

_____ steps

b. A spool holds 192 feet of rope. 54 feet was first cut off, then another 75 feet. How much rope is left on the spool?

_____ feet

c. Alisa has $75 saved. She has seen two guitars that she likes. The red guitar is $167 and the purple guitar is $135. A guitar strap costs $21. If Alisa wants the red guitar and the strap, how much more money does she need?

$_____

Step Ahead

Write a word problem to match this calculation.

127 + 48 then subtract 136

_____
_____
_____
_____

Think and Solve

Write how you can use **both** of these buckets to measure out exactly 7 liters of water to put into the tub.

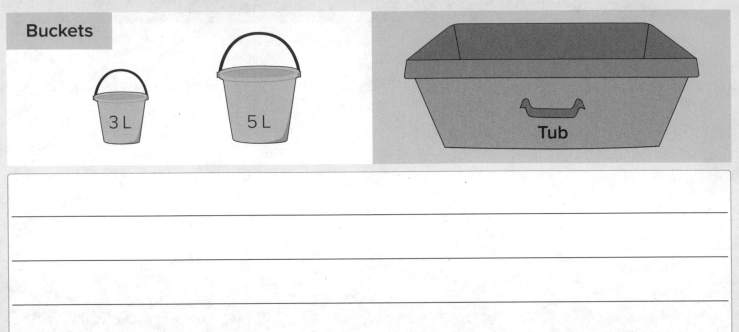

Buckets

3 L

5 L

Tub

Words at Work

Write a subtraction equation that uses the numbers 169 and 215.

Write a word problem to match your equation.
Then write how you find the solution

[ ] − [ ] = [ ]

© ORIGO Education

Ongoing Practice

1. Use what you can see to help write a fact family for each array.

a.

6 × 4 = _____

4 × 6 = _____

_____ ÷ _____ = _____

_____ ÷ _____ = _____

b.

4 × _____ = _____

_____ × 4 = _____

_____ ÷ _____ = _____

_____ ÷ _____ = _____

c.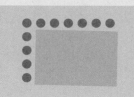

_____ × _____ = _____

_____ × _____ = _____

_____ ÷ _____ = _____

_____ ÷ _____ = _____

2. Use the count-on strategy to calculate the difference between these scores.
Draw jumps on the number line to show your thinking.

Difference _____

Preparing for Module 6

This table shows the favorite juice flavors of some Grade 3 students.

Juice	Number of Votes
Apple	8
Cranberry	9
Orange	4

Complete the bar graph to show the data.

Title: _____

Juice

0	1	2	3	4	5	6	7	8	9	10

Number of votes

Step In

What do you know about this array?

How can you figure out the total number of dots?

Write an equation to describe the array.

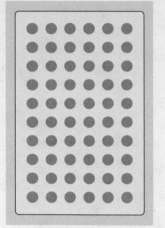

What do you know about this array?

How can you use the first array to figure out the total number of dots in this array?

I know 10 sixes is 60, so 9 sixes is 6 less. That's 54.

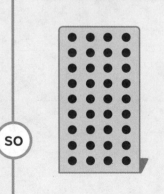

What other facts involving 9 could you solve using this strategy?

Step Up

1. Look at these pictures. Complete each pair of facts.

a.

 so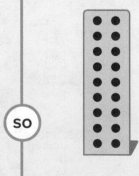

$10 \times 2 = $ ____ $9 \times 2 = $ ____

b.

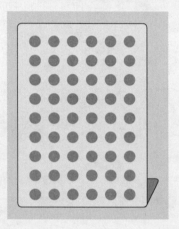 so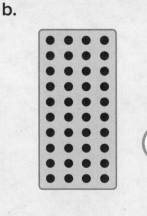

$10 \times 4 = $ ____ $9 \times 4 = $ ____

2. Write the product for the tens fact. Then use that fact to help you write the nines fact and its turnaround.

a.
10 × 3 = ☐

so

9 × 3 = _____

3 × ___ = _____

b.
10 × 5 = ☐

so

9 × 5 = _____

5 × ___ = _____

c.
10 × 4 = ☐

so

9 × 4 = _____

4 × ___ = _____

d.
10 × 7 = ☐

so

9 × ___ = _____

___ × ___ = _____

e.
10 × 6 = ☐

so

9 × ___ = _____

___ × ___ = _____

f.
10 × 8 = ☐

so

9 × ___ = _____

___ × ___ = _____

3. Color the ◯ beside the thinking you could use to calculate the product for the nines fact. Then write the product.

a.
9 × 7 = ☐

◯ 10 × 7 then subtract 7
◯ 10 × 7 then subtract 9
◯ 10 × 7 then subtract 10

b.
9 × 4 = ☐

◯ 10 × 4 then subtract 9
◯ 10 × 4 then subtract 4
◯ 10 × 9 then subtract 4

c.
9 × 8 = ☐

◯ 10 × 8 then subtract 9
◯ 10 × 8 then subtract 8
◯ 9 × 8 then subtract 10

Step Ahead

Amy figured out 3 × 9 like this. Describe her mistake in words.

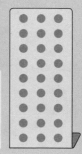

10 rows of 3 is 30, so 9 rows of 3 is 9 less. That is 21.

Step In Look at each of these nine facts.

$9 \times 3 = 27$ $9 \times 4 = 36$ $9 \times 5 = 45$

What do you notice about each product?

What happens when you add the two digits in each product?

When working with the nines multiplication facts, the digits in each product total 9.

I know that my nines fact is incorrect if the digits in the product do not total 9.

Write three more nines facts that you know. Then check to see if the digits in each product total 9.

☐ × ☐ = ☐   ☐ × ☐ = ☐   ☐ × ☐ = ☐

Step Up

1. Circle the facts that are incorrect.
   Write the facts so that they are correct.

a.
$9 \times 1 = 9$
$9 \times 2 = 18$
$9 \times 3 = 27$
$9 \times 4 = 36$
$9 \times 5 = 45$
$9 \times 6 = 54$
$9 \times 7 = 62$
$9 \times 8 = 72$
$9 \times 9 = 81$
$9 \times 10 = 90$

b.
$9 \times 1 = 9$
$9 \times 2 = 18$
$9 \times 3 = 27$
$9 \times 4 = 38$
$9 \times 5 = 45$
$9 \times 6 = 54$
$9 \times 7 = 63$
$9 \times 8 = 72$
$9 \times 9 = 81$
$9 \times 10 = 90$

c.
$9 \times 1 = 9$
$9 \times 2 = 18$
$9 \times 3 = 27$
$9 \times 4 = 36$
$9 \times 5 = 45$
$9 \times 6 = 54$
$9 \times 7 = 63$
$9 \times 8 = 72$
$9 \times 9 = 79$
$9 \times 10 = 90$

2. Color products that belong to a nines fact. Then write the matching nines facts.

a.

(72) (19) (45) (53) (90) (27) (60)

☐ × ☐ = ⬭   ☐ × ☐ = ⬭

☐ × ☐ = ⬭   ☐ × ☐ = ⬭

b.

(67) (9) (81) (71) (63) (54) (94)

☐ × ☐ = ⬭   ☐ × ☐ = ⬭

☐ × ☐ = ⬭   ☐ × ☐ = ⬭

3. Write a word problem to match this equation.

$6 \times 9 = ?$

Step Ahead

Complete the nines fact. Then use the product to help you complete the equation below.

a.

$3 \times 9 = $ ☐

$3 \times 90 = $ ☐

b.

$7 \times 9 = $ ☐

$7 \times 90 = $ ☐

c.

$9 \times 2 = $ ☐

$90 \times 2 = $ ☐

d.

$9 \times 8 = $ ☐

$90 \times 8 = $ ☐

Computation Practice

Cuddles the cat sleeps on the piano. Last night, a storm hit and the lights went out. Where was Cuddles when the lights went out?

★ Write each product and the turnaround fact. Then write each letter above its matching product in the grid below.

$4 \times 3 =$ ☐ $=$ ☐ $\times$ ☐ **h** $6 \times 4 =$ ☐ $=$ ☐ $\times$ ☐ **n**

$8 \times 4 =$ ☐ $=$ ☐ $\times$ ☐ **e** $4 \times 0 =$ ☐ $=$ ☐ $\times$ ☐ **a**

$4 \times 7 =$ ☐ $=$ ☐ $\times$ ☐ **i** $9 \times 4 =$ ☐ $=$ ☐ $\times$ ☐ **r**

$2 \times 4 =$ ☐ $=$ ☐ $\times$ ☐ **t** $4 \times 5 =$ ☐ $=$ ☐ $\times$ ☐ **k**

$4 \times 1 =$ ☐ $=$ ☐ $\times$ ☐ **d**

28   24   8   12   32   4   0   36   20

Complete these facts as fast as you can.

$8 \times 4 =$ ☐ $8 \times 8 =$ ☐ $5 \times 8 =$ ☐

$1 \times 8 =$ ☐ $7 \times 8 =$ ☐ $8 \times 9 =$ ☐

$8 \times 6 =$ ☐ $8 \times 2 =$ ☐ $3 \times 8 =$ ☐

Ongoing Practice

1. Complete these puzzles to show fractions to match. Each circle is one whole.

a.
$\dfrac{3}{4}$ | _____ **is shaded**

b.
two-sixths | **is not** shaded | ⬚

c.
$\dfrac{2}{3}$ | _____ **is shaded**

d.
five-eighths | **is not** shaded | ⬚

2. Color the ⬭ beside the thinking you could use to calculate the product for the nines fact. Then write the product.

a.
$9 \times 6 = \underline{\quad}$

○ 10×6 then subtract 6
○ 10×6 then subtract 9
○ 10×6 then subtract 10

b.
$9 \times 3 = \underline{\quad}$

○ 10×3 then subtract 9
○ 10×3 then subtract 10
○ 10×3 then subtract 3

c.
$9 \times 5 = \underline{\quad}$

○ 10×9 then subtract 9
○ 10×5 then subtract 5
○ 10×5 then subtract 10

Preparing for Module 7

Complete these equations.

a. $\boxed{} \times 5 = 5$

b. $5 \times \boxed{} = 25$

c. $\boxed{} \times 7 = 35$

d. $5 \times \boxed{} = 20$

e. $\boxed{} \times 3 = 15$

f. $5 \times 8 = \underline{\quad}$

g. $\boxed{} \times 5 = 30$

h. $5 \times 2 = \underline{\quad}$

Step In

What number should be written in the last space of each row across this hundred chart?

Write the numbers on the chart.

What are these numbers called?

If you start at 0 and count in steps of 9, what numbers will you say? Write the numbers in the hundred chart.

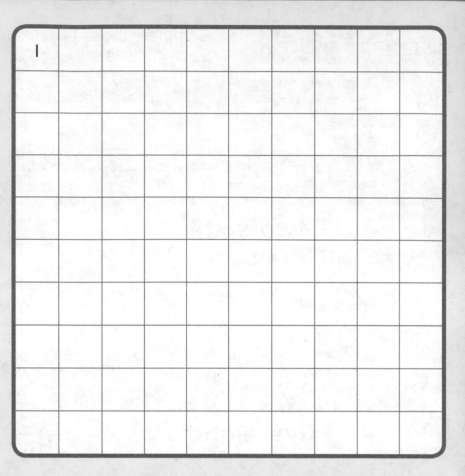

Look at the jumps of **9** along this number line.

Write the numbers in the boxes below.

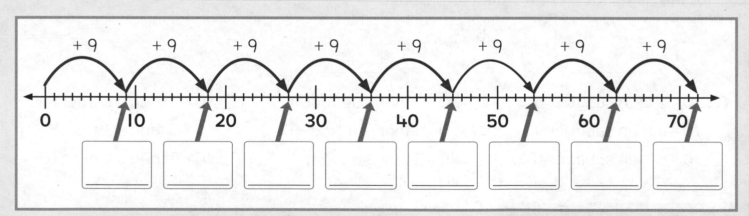

Look at the hundred chart and the number line.
What pattern do you notice?

How does the tens digit change?
How does the ones digit change?

Think about the nines multiplication facts.

1. Use what you now know to complete this pattern.

a. $10 - 1 = 1 \times 9$

b. $\boxed{} - \boxed{} = \boxed{} \times \boxed{}$

c. $\boxed{} - \boxed{} = \boxed{} \times \boxed{}$

d. $\boxed{} - \boxed{} = \boxed{} \times \boxed{}$

e. $\boxed{} - \boxed{} = \boxed{} \times \boxed{}$

f. $\boxed{} - \boxed{} = \boxed{} \times \boxed{}$

g. $\boxed{} - \boxed{} = \boxed{} \times \boxed{}$

h. $\boxed{} - \boxed{} = \boxed{} \times \boxed{}$

2. Use the pattern to help you complete these.

a. $8 \times 9 = \underline{}$

b. $10 \times 9 = \underline{}$

c. $13 \times 9 = \underline{}$

d. $12 \times 9 = \underline{}$

e. $15 \times 9 = \underline{}$

f. $18 \times 9 = \underline{}$

g. $17 \times 9 = \underline{}$

h. $14 \times 9 = \underline{}$

Step Ahead

These are the numbers you say when you start at 0 and count in steps of 9 to 90.

| 0 | 9 | 18 | 27 | 36 | 45 | 54 | 63 | 72 | 81 | 90 |

If you put these digits next to each other without changing their order, they make a large number that reads the same way forward or backward. This is called a **palindrome**.

Circle the numbers below that form a palindrome.

2 1 2 0 0 2   1 3 5 5 3 1   2 0 7 7 0 2

4 0 0 4 0 4   9 3 0 0 3 9   8 1 8 1 8 1

Step In   What is the total cost of 6 adult tickets?

What nearby fact could you use to help you figure out the total cost?

Bella buys 4 adult tickets and one child ticket. What is the total cost?

What equation could you write to show how you figured it out?

I'll call the cost of the tickets **t**.
t = 4 × 9 plus 4.

Emily buys 5 adult tickets and pays with a $50 bill. How could you calculate the amount of change she received?

TRAIN TICKETS

Child $4

Adult $9

Step Up   1.   Solve each problem. Show your thinking.

a. What is the total cost of 7 adult tickets?

$_____

b. What is the total cost of 3 child tickets and one senior ticket?

$_____

c. If you buy 2 weekend passes, how much change will you receive from $30?

$_____

COUNTY FAIR ADMISSION

Child	$4 each
Adult	$9 each
Senior	$5 each
Weekend Pass	$12 each

2. Use this information to answer Questions 2 and 3. Show your thinking.

RIDES

Zipper	6 tickets
Rocket	8 tickets
Carousel	4 tickets
Skyfly	10 tickets
Mega Drop	5 tickets

a. How many tickets are needed for 4 rides on the Zipper and one ride on the Skyfly?

_____ tickets

b. How many tickets are needed for 6 rides on the Rocket?

_____ tickets

c. How many tickets are needed for 2 rides on the Carousel and 2 rides on the Mega Drop?

_____ tickets

3. Juan started the day with 40 tickets. He spent all his tickets on one type of ride. How many times might he have gone on each of these rides?

a. Rocket	**b.** Carousel	**c.** Skyfly	**d.** Mega Drop
_____ times	_____ times	_____ times	_____ times

Step Ahead   There are 90 tickets on each roll.

Write an equation to calculate the number of tickets on 4 rolls.

_____ tickets

Think and Solve

 THINK TANK

Write the missing numbers below.

$$W + W = 16 \qquad W - Y = 3$$

a. $\boxed{W} + \boxed{Y} = \underline{}$

b. $\boxed{W} \times \boxed{Y} = \underline{}$

Words at Work

Write in words how you solve this problem.

Michelle's grandmother gave her $40 to spend at the county fair. Michelle had 6 rides on the Mega Drop and 4 rides on the Rollercoaster. Rides on the Mega Drop cost $5 each and rides on the Rollercoaster cost $8 each. She also bought lunch for $12. At the end of the day, she has $2 left. How much of her own money did she take to the fair?

1. The distance between 0 and 1 is one whole. Write the fraction shown by each jump. Then write the fraction in words.

a.

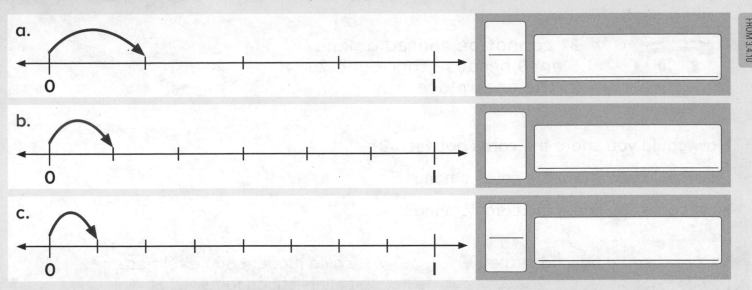

b.

c.

FROM 3.4.10

2. Complete the equations in the boxes below.

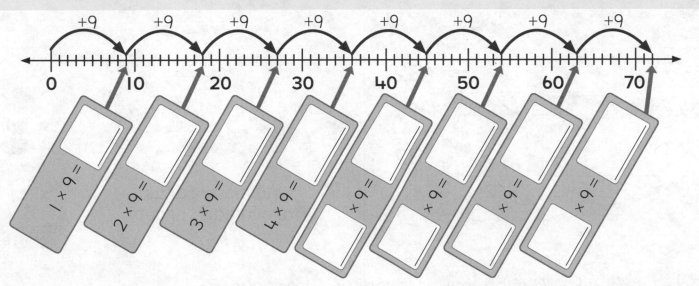

FROM 3.6.3

Preparing for Module 7

Read each problem. Then color the label to show your estimate.

a. One garden hose is 20 feet long. Another garden hose is 8 feet longer. About how long is the second hose?

| 10 ft | 20 ft | 30 ft |

b. Nam cycled for 23 minutes in the morning and 18 minutes in the afternoon. About how many minutes did he cycle that day?

| 30 min | 40 min | 50 min |

Step In

There are 32 cards in this pack. How could you share the cards into groups of equal size?

32 cannot be shared among 5 or 10 because there is a 2 in the ones place.

How could you share the cards between 2?

How could you share the cards among 4?

How could you share the cards among 8?

Corey used a halving strategy.

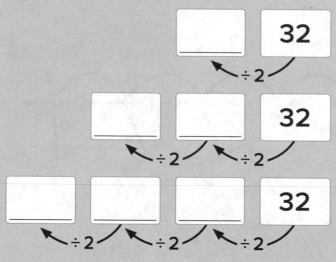

32 ÷ 2

32 ÷ 2 ÷ 2

32 ÷ 2 ÷ 2 ÷ 2

Kayla thought of the related multiplication facts.

$2 \times \boxed{} = 32$

$4 \times \boxed{} = 32$

$8 \times \boxed{} = 32$

How many cards are in each group?

Step Up

1. Write the number of cards in each share. Use cubes to help your thinking.

a.

$16 \div 2 = \boxed{}$

$16 \div 4 = \boxed{}$

$16 \div 8 = \boxed{}$

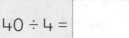
16 cards

b.

$40 \div 2 = \boxed{}$

$40 \div 4 = \boxed{}$

$40 \div 8 = \boxed{}$

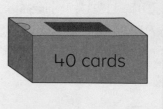
40 cards

2. Complete the multiplication fact you would use to figure out the division fact. Then complete the division fact.

a.

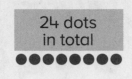
24 dots in total

____ × 8 = 24

24 ÷ 8 = ____

b.

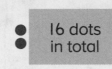
16 dots in total

2 × ____ = 16

16 ÷ 2 = ____

c.

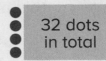
48 dots in total

6 × ____ = 48

48 ÷ 6 = ____

d.

32 dots in total

4 × ____ = 32

32 ÷ 4 = ____

e.

80 dots in total

____ × 8 = 80

80 ÷ 8 = ____

f.

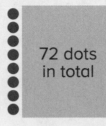
72 dots in total

8 × ____ = 72

72 ÷ 8 = ____

g.

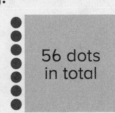
56 dots in total

7 × ____ = 56

56 ÷ 7 = ____

h.

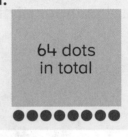
64 dots in total

____ × 8 = 64

64 ÷ 8 = ____

3. Write a multiplication and division fact to match each problem. Use a **?** to show the unknown amount.

a. Cars are parked in rows of 8. There are 56 cars. How many rows are there?

☐ × ☐ = ☐   ☐ ÷ ☐ = ☐

b. 32 people are at a diner. Each table seats 4 people. How many tables are there?

☐ × ☐ = ☐   ☐ ÷ ☐ = ☐

Step Ahead

Write an equation to show how you solve this problem.

Fatima earns $8 each week.
How many weeks will it take her to earn $72?

 weeks

Step In

Blake wrote four facts to match this picture of stickers.

8 × 5 = 40	40 ÷ 5 = 8
5 × 8 = 40	40 ÷ 8 = 5

STICKERS

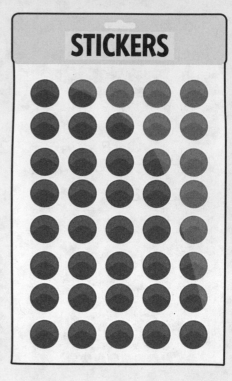

How does each fact match the picture?

Which facts are used to figure out the total number of stickers?

8 × 5 or 5 × 8.

What are the two division facts used to figure out?

How could you arrange 48 stickers into equal rows?

Draw a simple picture to show your thinking. Then write two multiplication facts and two related division facts to match the picture.

1. Color an array to match the numbers given.
   Then complete the matching fact family.

a.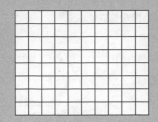

$8 \times 7 =$ _____

____ $\times$ ____ $=$ ____

____ $\div$ ____ $=$ ____

____ $\div$ ____ $=$ ____

b.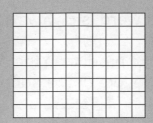

$3 \times 8 =$ _____

____ $\times$ ____ $=$ ____

____ $\div$ ____ $=$ ____

____ $\div$ ____ $=$ ____

c.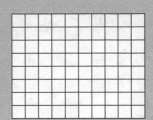

$8 \times 9 =$ _____

____ $\times$ ____ $=$ ____

____ $\div$ ____ $=$ ____

____ $\div$ ____ $=$ ____

2. Complete each equation. Then use the same color to show the number facts
   that belong in the same fact family.

$32 \div 4 = \boxed{}$

$\boxed{} = 56 \div 8$

$\boxed{} = 7 \times 8$

$72 \div 9 = \boxed{}$

$\boxed{} = 8 \times 7$

$72 \div \boxed{} = 9$

$32 = \boxed{} \times 8$

$\boxed{} = 16 \div 2$

$16 \div 8 = \boxed{}$

$\boxed{} = 2 \times 8$

$\boxed{} = 9 \times 8$

$8 \times 4 = \boxed{}$

Write the missing number in each fact.

a. $40 \div 5 = \boxed{}$

b. $16 \div \boxed{} = 2$

c. $\boxed{} \div 8 = 8$

d. $80 \div \boxed{} = 8$

e. $\boxed{} \div 8 = 4$

f. $9 = \boxed{} \div 8$

g. $48 \div \boxed{} = 6$

h. $\boxed{} = 56 \div 8$

Computation Practice — What word is always spelled incorrectly?

★ Complete the equations. Find each product in the grid below and cross out the letter above. Then write the remaining letters at the bottom of the page.

2 × 45 =	2 × 71 =	2 × 61 =
55 × 2 =	2 × 44 =	34 × 2 =
2 × 85 =	15 × 2 =	2 × 33 =
2 × 51 =	2 × 12 =	2 × 21 =
50 × 2 =	35 × 2 =	95 × 2 =
2 × 43 =	75 × 2 =	2 × 60 =
54 × 2 =	2 × 63 =	64 × 2 =
2 × 72 =		

✳

I	N	E	R	R	O	R	C	E	N	T
106	84	66	102	90	150	144	104	122	120	24
O	R	F	U	L	L	Y	R	U	S	H
64	76	30	128	142	42	68	124	170	108	70
E	C	C	E	P	T	T	A	L	L	Y
60	110	80	100	126	82	88	86	78	190	92

Write the remaining letters in order from the ✳ to the bottom-right corner.

I. On each number line, the distance from 0 to I is one whole. Look at how each number line has been split. Write the fraction each arrow is pointing to.

a.

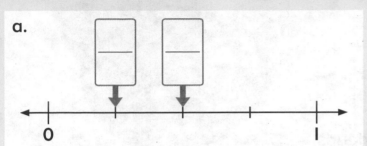

b.

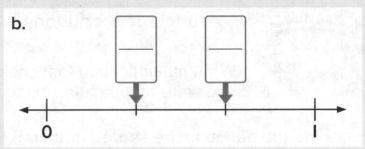

2. Solve each problem. Show your thinking.

a. Kylie bought 3 books for $8 each and 2 books for $7 each. What is the total cost of her purchase?

$_____

b. Kevin bought 5 books for $9 each and 3 books for $5 each. How much change will he get from $100?

$_____

Preparing for Module 7 Calculate each sum.

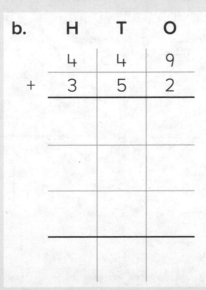

a.

H	T	O
2	3	5
+ 1	1	6
	1	1
	4	0
3	0	0

b.

H	T	O
4	4	9
+ 3	5	2

c.

H	T	O
5	6	0
+ 1	9	7

Step In

What do you see in this picture?

I bunch of 5 balloons.

What multiplication fact could you write to match this picture?

Imagine the balloons are shared among 5 friends.
How many balloons will they each have?

What division fact could you write?

5 balloons shared among 5 friends is I balloon each, so 5 ÷ 5 = I.

What multiplication fact could you write to match this picture?

Imagine that all these blocks are given to one student. What division fact could you write to describe the sharing?

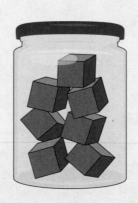

7 blocks are given to I student. She now has 7 blocks, so 7 ÷ I = 7.

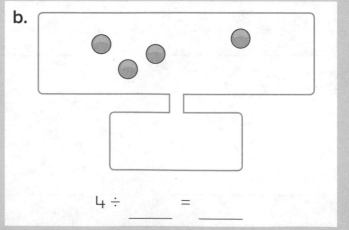

Step Up

I. Imagine these counters are shared into equal groups. Complete the division facts to match.

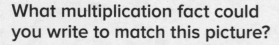

a.

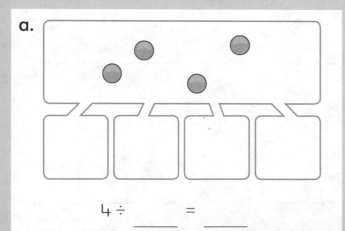

4 ÷ _____ = _____

b.

4 ÷ _____ = _____

2. Write the division fact to match. You can draw counters to help.

a.

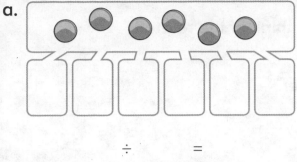

___ ÷ ___ = ___

b.

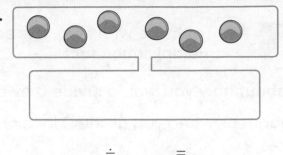

___ ÷ ___ = ___

c.

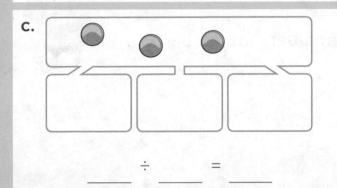

___ ÷ ___ = ___

d.

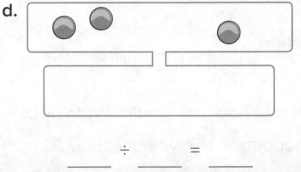

___ ÷ ___ = ___

3. Complete each fact. Then write how you figured out the missing numbers.

a.
1 ÷ 1 =

2 ÷ 1 =

3 ÷ 1 =

4 ÷ 1 =

8 ÷ 1 =

10 ÷ 1 =

b.
1 ÷ 1 =

2 ÷ 2 =

3 ÷ 3 =

4 ÷ 4 =

7 ÷ 7 =

9 ÷ 9 =

Step Ahead   Use the rules you wrote in Question 3 to calculate each of these.

a.
37 ÷ 1 =

b.
101 ÷ 101 =

c.
53 ÷ 53 =

d.
132 ÷ 1 =

Step In

To divide with zero, it is easier to think of the related multiplication fact.

Think about how you would divide 0 by a number.

What happens when you divide 0 by a number?

see → $0 \div 6 = \boxed{}$

think → $6 \times \boxed{} = 0$

The answer **has to be 0.**

Think about how you would divide by 0.

What happens when you divide by 0?

see → $6 \div 0 = \boxed{}$

think → $0 \times \boxed{} = 6$

A number multiplied by 0 is 0, so $6 \div 0$ is **not possible.**

What happens when you divide 0 by 0?

see → $0 \div 0 = \boxed{}$

think → $0 \times \boxed{} = 0$

$0 \times 9 = 0$ and $0 \times 194 = 0$, so 0 multiplied by any number equals 0. Therefore, the answer to $0 \div 0$ **cannot be decided.**

Step Up

1. Write numbers to complete these facts.

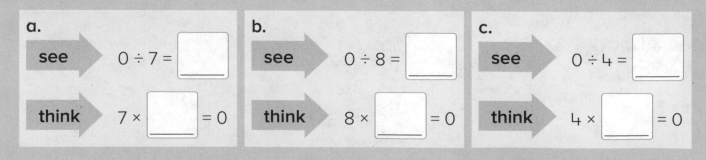

a.

see → $0 \div 7 = \boxed{}$

think → $7 \times \boxed{} = 0$

b.

see → $0 \div 8 = \boxed{}$

think → $8 \times \boxed{} = 0$

c.

see → $0 \div 4 = \boxed{}$

think → $4 \times \boxed{} = 0$

2. For each of these, color the ⬭ beside the best description of the quotient.

a. $4 \div 0$
- ⬭ not possible
- ⬭ has to be 0
- ⬭ cannot be decided

b. $0 \div 9$
- ⬭ not possible
- ⬭ has to be 0
- ⬭ cannot be decided

c. $7 \div 0$
- ⬭ not possible
- ⬭ has to be 0
- ⬭ cannot be decided

d. $5 \div 0$
- ⬭ not possible
- ⬭ has to be 0
- ⬭ cannot be decided

e. $0 \div 3$
- ⬭ not possible
- ⬭ has to be 0
- ⬭ cannot be decided

f. $0 \div 0$
- ⬭ not possible
- ⬭ has to be 0
- ⬭ cannot be decided

g. $0 \div 1$
- ⬭ not possible
- ⬭ has to be 0
- ⬭ cannot be decided

h. $0 \div 10$
- ⬭ not possible
- ⬭ has to be 0
- ⬭ cannot be decided

i. $2 \div 0$
- ⬭ not possible
- ⬭ has to be 0
- ⬭ cannot be decided

Step Ahead   Use a calculator to figure out each product.
Then write what you notice.

$2 \times 5 \times 3 \times 4 \times 0 = \boxed{}$

$0 \times 4 \times 3 \times 2 \times 5 = \boxed{}$

$5 \times 3 \times 0 \times 4 \times 2 = \boxed{}$

_____
_____
_____

Think and Solve Look at this arrow diagram.

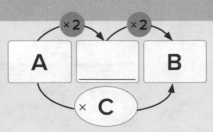

Write the missing numbers below.

a.

If A = 5, then B = _____

b.

If A = 7, then B = _____

c.

If A = 9, then B = _____

d.

If A = 12, then B = _____

e.

C = _____

Words at Work

Imagine your friend was away from school when you learned about the zeros division facts. Write how you would explain why $7 \div 0$ is not possible to your friend.

_____

_____

_____

_____

_____

_____

_____

Ongoing Practice

1. Count back to calculate each difference. Draw jumps on the number line to show your thinking.

a.

$75 - 28 = $ ☐

⟵————————————————————————⟶

b.

$91 - 25 = $ ☐

⟵————————————————————————⟶

2. Write the missing numbers.

a.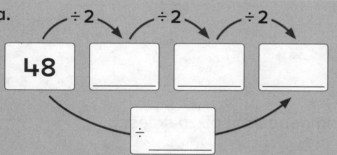

b.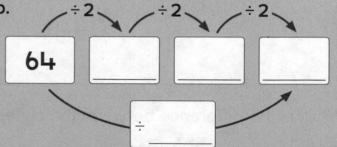

Preparing for Module 7

Calculate each sum. Draw jumps on the number line to show your thinking.

a.

$38 + 37 = $ ☐

⟵————————————————————————⟶

b.

$45 + 36 = $ ☐

⟵————————————————————————⟶

Step In What do you notice about this graph?

| | | | means 10 pizzas |

Pizza Sales

Type of pizza									
Cheese	🍕	🍕	🍕	🍕	🍕	🍕			
Pepperoni	🍕	🍕	🍕	🍕	🍕				

What does represent? What does represent?

How could you represent 25 pizza sales? Draw a picture.

What is the difference between the cheese and pepperoni pizza sales?

What equation could you write?

How could you figure out the total pizza sales?

Step Up

1. This table shows the pizza sales for 5 days. Complete the graph at the top of page 221 to show the results.

Day	Total Sales
Monday	75
Tuesday	40
Wednesday	35
Thursday	50
Friday	90

Pizza Sales   ⬤ means 10 pizzas

Day										
Monday										
Tuesday										
Wednesday										
Thursday										
Friday										

2. Look at the graph above.

a. On what day were the most pizzas sold? _____

b. How many pizzas were sold before Thursday? _____

c. How many more pizzas were sold on Friday than Wednesday? _____

d. How many pizzas were sold in 5 days? _____

e. How many more pizzas were sold on Thursday and Friday than on Monday and Tuesday? _____

Step Ahead   Read the clues. Then write the missing labels.

Pizza Sales   🍕 means 10 pizzas

Clues
- There were fewer **cheese** pizzas sold than **pepperoni** pizzas.
- There were double the number of **supreme** pizzas sold than **pepperoni** pizzas.

Step In What does this bar graph tell you?

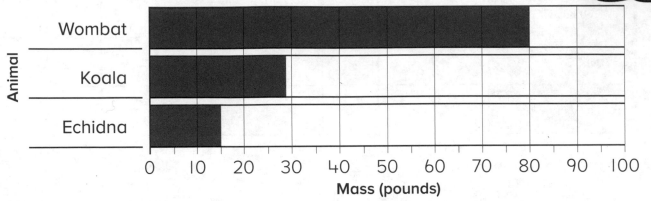

Mass of Native Australian Animals

Animal: Wombat, Koala, Echidna

Mass (pounds): 0, 10, 20, 30, 40, 50, 60, 70, 80, 90, 100

What do you notice about the numbers written along the horizontal axis?

What do the marks between the numbers tell you?

How could you figure out the mass of each animal?

Compare the mass of the wombat to that of the other animals.

> The numbers written along the horizontal axis or baseline are called a **scale**.

How much more does the wombat weigh?

What is the difference in mass between the koala and the echidna?

Step Up I. This table shows the mass of some American animals. Complete the bar graph at the top of page 223 to show the results.

Animal	Mass (pounds)
Raccoon	32
Beaver	55
Wolf	89
Coyote	50

Title: _____

Animal

_____

_____

_____

_____

0   10   20   30   40   50   60   70   80   90   100

Mass (pounds)

2. a. Which two animals are of similar mass?

b. Which three animals have a total mass of about 150 pounds?

c. What is the difference in mass between the wolf and raccoon? _____ lb

d. What is the difference in mass between the beaver and wolf? _____ lb

e. What is the total mass of the beaver, wolf, and coyote? _____ lb

Step Ahead

A vet has scales that can measure up to 200 pounds. What is the greatest number of raccoons that could be weighed at the same time? Show your thinking.

_____

Computation Practice   What animal is best at baseball?

★ Complete the equations. Then find each total in the grid below and cross out the letter above.

124 + 39 = _____

247 + 28 = _____

359 + 38 = _____

19 + 346 = _____

19 + 167 = _____

156 + 28 = _____

238 + 39 = _____

49 + 418 = _____

29 + 249 = _____

38 + 229 = _____

167 + 29 = _____

338 + 29 = _____

145 + 48 = _____

256 + 38 = _____

18 + 158 = _____

28 + 269 = _____

368 + 19 = _____

218 + 29 = _____

347 + 28 = _____

48 + 149 = _____

Write the remaining letters in order from the ✳ to the bottom-right corner.

✳	A	F	O	X	I	E	I	T	B	I	R	D
	187	365	294	186	163	278	267	176	198	184	247	196
	A	B	E	A	R	Y	C	A	T	A	N	T
	193	275	387	375	397	367	297	276	467	197	277	366

Ongoing Practice

1. Calculate the amount left on the gift card.
Draw jumps on the number line to show your thinking.

a.

$185
Gift Card

$67

$ _____

b.

$250
Gift Card

$114

$ _____

2. Look at this graph.

🍕 means 10 pizzas

Pizza Sales

Type of pizza								
Pepperoni	🍕	🍕	🍕	🍕	🍕	🍕	🍕	
Cheese	🍕	🍕	🍕	🍕	🍕			
Veggie	🍕	🍕	🍕	🍕	🍕	🍕		

a. How many cheese pizzas were sold? _____

b. How many more veggie pizzas were sold than cheese pizzas? _____

c. What is the difference between the cheese and pepperoni pizza sales? _____

Preparing for Module 7

Calculate the sum. Draw jumps on the number line to show your thinking.

$187 + 62 =$ _____

Data: Working with line plots

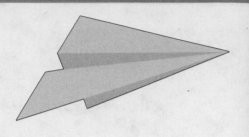

Step In

Students in Class 3a investigate the distance their paper planes can fly. Each distance is rounded to the nearest yard.

This line plot shows the results.

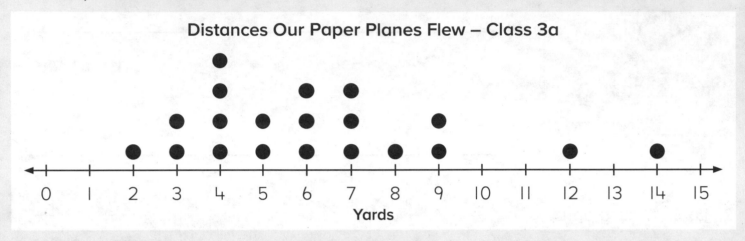

Distances Our Paper Planes Flew – Class 3a

Yards

How far did most of the paper planes fly?

How many paper planes flew a distance of more than 7 yards?

> Line plots are sometimes called dot plots. They are useful for showing the shape of a data set.

How many paper planes flew a distance of more than 3 yards, but fewer than 9 yards?

What else can you share about the results?

Step Up

These results are from Class 3b. Use them to complete the line plot on page 227.

Distances Our Paper Planes Flew – Class 3b				
2 yards	7 yards	5 yards	5 yards	11 yards
6 yards	8 yards	13 yards	6 yards	4 yards
3 yards	6 yards	11 yards	8 yards	7 yards
6 yards	5 yards	4 yards	7 yards	6 yards

l. Draw ◯ to match the results on page 226. Cross out each length in the table on page 226 after you record it in the line plot.

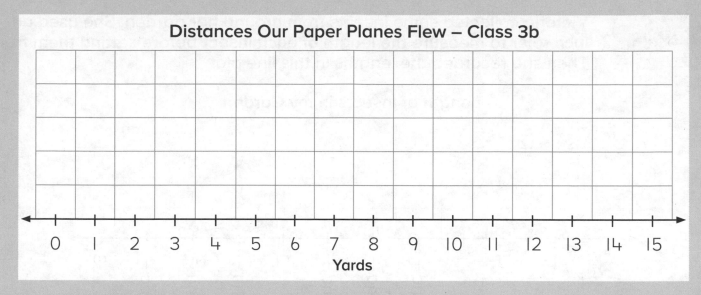

Distances Our Paper Planes Flew – Class 3b

Yards

2. Look at the line plot above.

    a. How many students are in Class 3b?

    b. How many paper planes flew fewer than 8 yards?

    c. How many paper planes flew a distance of more than 4 yards, but fewer than 8 yards?

    d. How many more paper planes flew a distance of 6 yards than 11 yards?

    e. What distance did most paper planes fly? _____ yd

Step Ahead

The principal wants to award a prize to the class that is best at making paper planes. She decides to close her eyes and choose one paper plane each from 3a and 3b. She then throws each plane to see which travels farther.

Which class do you think will win? Explain your thinking.

_____

_____

Step In

Victoria collected some insects from around her garden. She used an inch ruler to measure the length of each insect before setting them free. Then she recorded the lengths in this line plot.

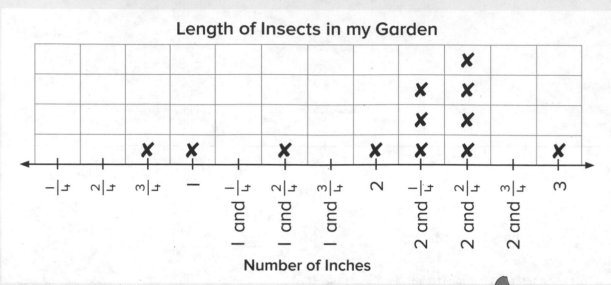

Length of Insects in my Garden

Number of Inches

Use your inch ruler to measure the length of this insect.

Is it closer to 2 inches long or 2 and $\frac{1}{4}$ inches long?

Draw an ✗ on the line plot to show the length of the insect.

What is the length of the longest insect recorded on the line plot?

What length was recorded the greatest number of times?

How many insects are 2 and $\frac{1}{4}$ inches long?
How many are shorter than 2 inches?

What is the total number of lengths recorded on the line plot?

Step Up

1. Your teacher will give your group some pieces of dry spaghetti. Use your inch ruler to measure the length of 20 pieces. Round each length to the nearest fourth of an inch. Use tallies to record the lengths on this chart.

$\frac{1}{4}$	$\frac{2}{4}$	$\frac{3}{4}$	1	1 and $\frac{1}{4}$	1 and $\frac{2}{4}$	1 and $\frac{3}{4}$	2	2 and $\frac{1}{4}$	2 and $\frac{2}{4}$	2 and $\frac{3}{4}$	3

2. Look at the tally chart in Question 1 on page 228.
Draw an ✗ on the line plot below to show each length.

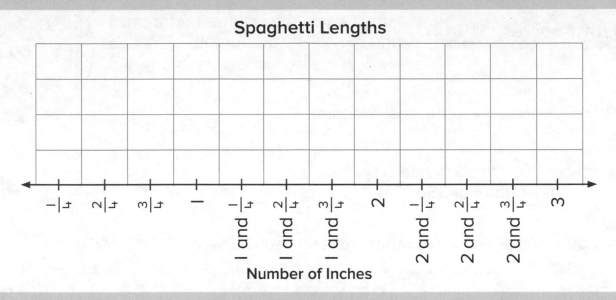

3. Look at the line plot in Question 2.
Complete each question.

a. Which lengths were recorded most often?

b. How many pieces were longer than 2 inches?

c. How many pieces were shorter than 1 and $\frac{3}{4}$ inches?

d. Imagine that you closed your eyes to choose one length of spaghetti.
How long do you think the piece of spaghetti might be? Explain your thinking.

Step Ahead Compare your results with those of another group. Were your
spaghetti lengths longer or shorter? Write your thinking in words.

Think and Solve   Imagine you threw three beanbags and they all hit this target.

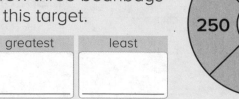

greatest   least

a. Write the greatest and least possible totals.

b. Write an equation to show one way you can make a **total of 350**.

☐ + ☐ + ☐ = **350**

c. Write equations to show **two other ways** you can make a total of 350.

☐ + ☐ + ☐ = **350**   ☐ + ☐ + ☐ = **350**

Words at Work Write the answer for each clue in the grid. Use words from the list. Some words are not used.

Clues Across

1. The horizontal ___ of a graph can be called the baseline.

4. You can build ___ from a tens fact to calculate the product of a nines fact.

6. ___ plots can be called dot plots.

Clues Down

2. The numbers written along the horizontal axis of a graph are called a ___.

3. A picture in a picture graph can represent ___ than one.

5. A nines fact is incorrect if the digits in the product do not total ___.

scale
ten
line
more
many
down
nine
axis

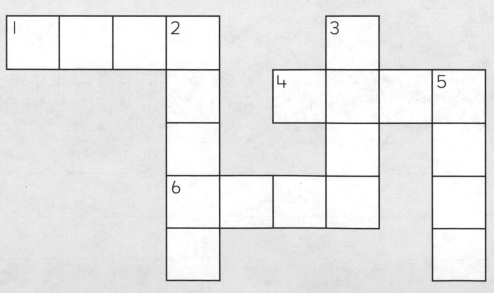

1. Calculate each difference. Show your thinking.

a.

$315 - 48 =$ ☐

FROM 3.5.11

b.

$353 - 197 =$ ☐

FROM 3.6.11

2. Look at this line plot.

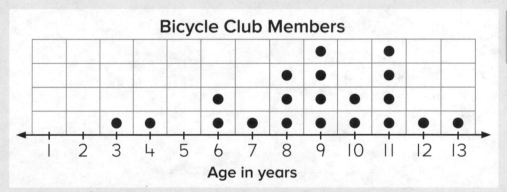

Bicycle Club Members

Age in years

a. Which ages were recorded most often?

☐

b. How many members were younger than 7 years? ☐

c. Draw more ● to show these new members.

| Lorena | Michelle | Darriel |
| 7 years old | 8 years old | 13 years old |

Preparing for Module 7

For each number, write the **ten** that is closest. You can use the number line to help.

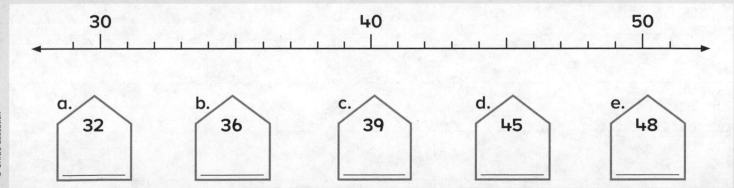

30   40   50

a. 32

b. 36

c. 39

d. 45

e. 48

STUDENT GLOSSARY

Algorithm

Algorithms are rules used for completing tasks or for solving problems. There are standard algorithms for calculating answers to addition, subtraction, multiplication and division problems. This example shows the addition algorithm.

H	T	O
1		
	9	2
+	3	6
1	2	8

Area

Area is the amount of surface that a shape covers. This amount is usually described in square units such as square centimeters (sq cm) or square inches (sq in).

Capacity

Capacity is the amount something can hold.

A **gallon** is a customary unit of capacity. The short way to write gallon is **gal**.

A **liter** is a metric unit of capacity. The short way to write liter is **L**.

A **pint** is a unit of capacity. There are 2 pints in one quart.
The short way to write pint is **pt**.

A **quart** is a unit of capacity. There are 4 quarts in one gallon.
The short way to write quart is **qt**.

Common Fraction

$\frac{2}{3}$ is shaded

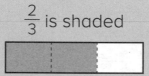

Common fractions describe equal parts of a whole. In this common fraction, 2 is the numerator and 3 is the denominator.

The **denominator** shows the number of equal parts (3) in the whole.
The **numerator** shows the number of those parts (2).

Unit fractions are common fractions that have a numerator of 1.

Proper fractions are common fractions that have a numerator that is less than the denominator. For example, $\frac{2}{5}$ is a proper fraction.

Improper fractions are common fractions that have a numerator that is greater than or equal to the denominator. For example, $\frac{7}{5}$ and $\frac{4}{4}$ are improper fractions.

Equivalent fractions are fractions that cover the same amount of area on a shape or are located on the same point on a number line.

For example: $\frac{1}{2}$ is equivalent to $\frac{2}{4}$

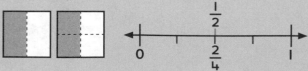

STUDENT GLOSSARY

Comparing

When read from left to right, the symbol > means **is greater than**.
The symbol < means **is less than**.
For example: 2 < 6 **means** 2 is less than 6

Division

Division is finding the number of equal groups or the number in each equal group when the total and one of these is known. For example, 8 ÷ __ = 4 or 8 ÷ 2 = __. This is recorded in a division equation that uses words or the ÷ symbol. The result of division is called the **quotient**.

Expanded form

A method of writing numbers as the sum of the values of each digit.
For example: $4,912 = (4 \times 1,000) + (9 \times 100) + (1 \times 10) + (2 \times 1)$

Fact family

A multiplication **fact family** includes a multiplication fact, its turnaround fact, and the two related division facts.
For example:

$$4 \times 2 = 8$$
$$2 \times 4 = 8$$
$$8 \div 4 = 2$$
$$8 \div 2 = 4$$

Length

Length is the measure of how long something is.

A **centimeter** is a metric unit of length. The short way to write centimeter is **cm**.

A **meter** is a metric unit of length. The short way to write meter is **m**.

Line plot

A **line plot** is used to show data.
On this line plot, each dot represents one student.

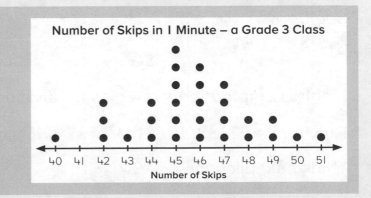

Number of Skips in 1 Minute – a Grade 3 Class
Number of Skips

Mass

Mass is the amount something weighs.

A **gram** is a metric unit of mass. There are 1,000 grams in one kilogram.

The short way to write gram is **g**.

A **kilogram** is a metric unit of mass. The short way to write kilogram is **kg**.

Mental computation strategies for multiplication

Strategies you can use to figure out a mathematical problem in your head.

Use ten
See 5×7 *think* half of 10×7

Doubling
See 2×7 *think* double 7
See 2×14 *think* double 14
See 4×7 *think* double, double 7
See 4×15 *think* double, double 15
See 8×7 *think* double, double, double 7
See 8×16 *think* double, double, double 16

Double and halve (associative property)
See 6×35 *think* double 3×70

Partial products (distributive property)
See 3×45 *think* $(3 \times 40) + (3 \times 5)$

Use a known fact
See 6×8 *think* $5 \times 8 + 8$
See 3×9 *think* $3 \times 10 - 3$

Mental computation strategies for division

Halving *See* $32 \div 4$ *think* half of 32 is 16, half of 16 is 8

Think multiplication *See* $30 \div 5$ *think* $5 \times 6 = 30$, so $30 \div 5 = 6$

STUDENT GLOSSARY

Multiplication

Multiplication is finding the total when the number of equal groups or rows and the number in each group or row are known. This is recorded in a multiplication equation that uses the × symbol. The result of multiplication is called the **product**.

Perimeter

A **perimeter** is the boundary of a shape and the total length of that boundary. For example, the perimeter of this rectangle is 20 inches.

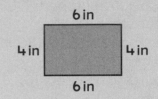

Order of operations

If there is **one** type of operation in a sentence, work left to right.

If there is **more than one** type of operation, work left to right in this **order**:

1. Perform any operation inside parentheses.

2. Multiply or divide pairs of numbers.

3. Add or subtract pairs of numbers.

Polyhedron

A **polyhedron** is any closed 3D object that has four or more flat faces.

When two surfaces meet, they make an **edge**.
When three or more edges meet, they make a **vertex**.

A **prism** is a polyhedron that has two identical faces that are joined by square or non-square rectangles. For example:

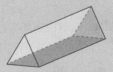

A **pyramid** is a polyhedron that has any polygon for a base. All the other faces joined to the base are triangles that meet at a point. For example:

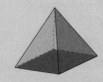

Quadrilateral

A **quadrilateral** is any polygon (closed 2D shape) that has 4 straight sides.
Any quadrilateral that has all corners the same in size is called a **rectangle**.
Any quadrilateral that has all side the same in length is called a **rhombus**.

TEACHER INDEX

Academic Vocabulary 16, 28, 40, 54, 66, 78, 92, 104, 116, 130, 142, 154, 168, 180, 192, 206, 218, 230, 254, 266, 278, 292, 304, 316, 330, 342, 354, 368, 381, 392, 406, 418, 430, 444, 456, 468

Addition
Associative property 355, 382, 383
Basic facts 10, 61
Common fractions 150, 151
Estimating 207, 258, 259, 262–71, 273
Four-digit numbers 102, 103, 111, 451
Language 46
Mental strategies
    Compensation 274–6, 299, 305
    Doubles 55, 61, 174, 324
    Place value 17, 46, 50, 51, 55–7, 125
Patterns 11, 44, 45, 49
Three-digit numbers 17, 50–7, 98, 125, 131, 137, 213, 224, 225, 230, 262–5, 269, 270, 271, 273–9, 287, 293, 299, 305, 310, 381, 387, 393, 462, 451
Two-digit numbers 22, 23, 34, 40, 44–9, 55, 61, 72, 92, 174, 219, 256, 257, 264, 265, 267, 268, 269, 274, 275, 278, 293, 324, 393
Word problems 23, 56, 57, 61, 137, 276, 277, 287, 305
Written methods
    Informal 52, 53, 56, 57, 131, 213, 262
    Standard algorithm 262–5, 268–71, 273, 276, 278, 279, 287, 293, 381, 387, 393

Algebraic thinking
Equality 44, 116, 245, 304, 313, 330, 368, 418, 468
Order of operations 384, 385, 388–92, 401, 407, 413
Patterns
    Addition 11, 44, 45, 49
    Division 215
    Multiplication 25, 164, 165, 202, 203, 247
    Shape 78
Problem solving
    Think Tank problems 16, 28, 40, 54, 66, 78, 92, 104, 116, 130, 142, 154, 168, 180, 192, 206, 218, 230, 254, 266, 278, 292, 304, 330, 342, 354, 368, 381, 392, 406, 418, 430, 444, 456, 468

Algebraic thinking (continued)
Word problems
    Addition 137, 207, 276, 277, 287, 305
    Area 372, 373, 380, 466, 467
    Capacity 315, 428, 429, 463
    Common fractions 151, 352–4
    Division 127, 129, 133, 143, 209, 289, 292
    Mass 314, 315, 342
    Multiplication 24, 25, 28, 33, 35, 39, 66, 85, 95, 97, 100, 101, 104, 105, 169, 176, 177, 180, 181, 199, 204, 205, 256, 257, 289, 343, 377
    Perimeter 466, 467, 469
    Subtraction 179, 183, 185, 190–2, 287
    Two-step 47, 137, 177, 190, 191, 206, 207, 213, 256, 257, 276, 277, 373, 380, 390–2, 401, 413
Using symbol for unknown 101, 105, 127, 129, 135, 142, 143, 176, 177, 181, 190, 199, 204, 209, 256, 289, 343, 385, 401

Comparing
3D objects 454, 455, 458, 459
Angles 448, 449
Capacity 23, 393, 426, 427, 457
Common fractions 294, 295, 301, 340, 341, 344–7, 349–55
Mass 11, 17
Money 33
Number
    Five-digit numbers 404, 405
    Four-digit numbers 108, 109, 163
    Three-digit numbers 67, 106–9, 230, 266
    Two-digit numbers 40, 73

Data
Bar graph 79, 154, 193, 222, 223, 425, 469
Interpreting 73, 79, 154, 220–3, 225–9, 231, 431, 469
Line plot 226–9, 231, 431
Picture graph
    Many-to-one 220, 221, 225, 419, 430
    One-to-one 73, 187
Sorting 77
Tally chart 187

© ORIGO Education

TEACHER INDEX

Division

Basic facts

All facts 412

Eights 208–11, 219, 298, 363, 386

Fives 128, 129, 132, 133, 175, 187, 193, 331, 348, 450

Fours 134, 135, 138, 139, 142, 181, 187, 193, 208, 260, 298, 331, 348, 386, 450

Nines 282, 283, 287, 369, 375

Ones 214, 215

Sevens 289, 290, 291, 299

Sixes 288, 289, 290, 291, 292, 293, 299

Tens 132, 133

Threes 289, 291, 299

Twos 134, 135, 138, 139, 181, 187, 208, 260, 298, 348, 386, 450

Zeros 216, 217, 218

Estimating 442, 443, 451

Language 120, 122

Mental strategies

Halving (and repeated halving) 30, 31, 36, 37, 134, 135, 142, 208, 349, 401

Think multiplication 126–9, 132, 134, 135, 138, 139, 142, 175, 208–11, 216, 217, 260, 282–5, 288–91, 293, 298, 299, 331, 348, 363, 369, 375, 386, 412, 440, 441, 444, 446, 447

Models

Equal groups (quotition model) 87, 120, 121, 125, 214

Sharing (partition model) 120, 121, 214, 215, 434, 435, 436, 437, 439

Patterns 215

Related to multiplication 30, 31, 122, 123, 126–35, 137–9, 142, 143, 175, 181, 187, 193, 208–11, 214, 216, 260, 282–5, 288–91, 293, 298, 299, 331, 348, 363, 369, 375, 386, 412, 440, 441, 444, 446, 447

Symbol 120

Two-digit numbers 30, 31, 349, 401, 434–7, 439–47, 457

Word problems 209, 289, 292, 442, 443, 447, 451

Estimating

Addition 207, 256–9, 262–71, 273

Division 442, 443

Multiplication 378, 379

Estimating (continued)

Subtraction 320, 321, 323, 325, 327, 328, 329, 332, 333, 335

Fact family

Multiplication and division 122, 123, 130–3, 137–9, 187, 193, 210, 211, 285, 290, 331, 363, 375

Fractions

Common fractions

Addition 150, 151, 261

Comparing 93, 147, 153, 294, 295, 301, 340, 341, 344–7, 349, 350, 351, 354, 355

Equivalent 93, 302–4, 306, 307, 317, 341

Improper fractions 294–7, 300, 301, 305, 307, 346, 347, 351

Language 140, 141, 144, 294–6, 302, 306, 316

Models

Area 93, 140, 141, 149, 152–4, 201, 296, 297, 311, 316, 392, 406

Length 87, 117, 141, 152–4, 294, 295, 302, 303, 305, 317, 340, 341

Number line 146, 147, 152–5, 207, 267, 273, 300, 301, 306, 307, 311, 317, 344–7, 349, 350, 351, 355

Unit fractions 117, 140, 141, 146, 147, 152, 153, 155, 207, 261, 340, 341, 344, 345, 349, 350

Word problems 151, 352–4

Measurement

Area

Composite shapes 249, 370, 371, 375, 392

Customary 358, 359

Metric 360, 361, 363, 392

Regular shapes 255, 261, 325, 358–61, 363–9, 378, 379, 431

Related to perimeter 464, 465

Rule for calculating 364–9

Word problems 372, 373, 380, 466, 467

Capacity

Comparing 23, 309, 393, 422, 423, 426, 427, 457

Customary 29, 245, 393, 422, 423, 426, 427, 457, 463

Language 426

© ORIGO Education

TEACHER INDEX

Measurement (continued)

Metric 308, 309, 325, 331
Word problems 192, 309, 315, 428, 429, 463

Length
Customary 226–9, 320, 321
Data 226–9, 469
Language 104, 266
Metric 266, 451
Word problems 266

Mass
Comparing 11, 17
Customary 11, 222, 223
Data 222, 223
Language 279, 312
Metric 17, 279, 312, 313, 337, 342, 343, 368, 456
Word problems 314, 315, 342

Perimeter
Irregular polygons 460, 461, 463
Language 460, 464
Regular polygons 460, 461
Related to area 464, 465
Word problems 466, 467, 469

Time
Duration 68, 69, 355
Language 58, 64, 65
Minutes 29, 35, 58, 59, 62, 63, 67, 73, 79, 349, 355
Word problems 59, 65, 66, 68, 69

Money

Cents 33, 61, 67, 381, 414–7, 439
Comparing 33
Dollars 67, 127, 129, 381, 414–7, 439
Transactions 61, 142, 143, 387, 416, 417, 420, 421, 445

Multiplication

Basic facts
All facts 250–3, 261, 336, 400, 407, 412, 438
Eights 158–61, 163–5, 168, 169, 175, 180, 200, 209–11, 248, 286, 298, 363, 380, 386, 463
Fives 36–9, 105, 124, 136, 148, 162, 169, 193, 201, 244–9, 255, 331, 348

Multiplication (continued)

Fours 90–5, 99, 111, 125, 131, 148, 158–61, 163, 168, 169, 175, 187, 193, 200, 218, 260, 298, 331, 348, 386, 463
Nines 196–9, 201–3, 248, 249, 282–5, 287, 369, 374, 375
Ones 166, 167, 172, 173, 181, 214
Sevens 250, 251, 254, 289–91, 299
Sixes 244–9, 255, 288–91, 290, 291, 293, 299, 374
Tens 32, 33, 36–9, 99, 163, 196, 197, 469
Threes 250, 251, 289, 291, 299
Twos 82–5, 87, 93–5, 99, 111, 124, 148, 158–63, 168, 169, 175, 187, 260, 298, 348, 386
Zeros 170–3, 175, 216, 217
Estimating 378, 379
Mental strategies
Build down 196, 197, 201–3, 248, 249
Build up 244, 246, 247, 249, 255
Double and halve 367, 382, 383, 393
Doubling (and repeated doubling) 82–5, 87–97, 99, 111, 125, 131, 158, 159, 212, 349, 354, 457
Use ten 36–8
Language 24
Models
Array 26, 27, 33, 36, 37, 49, 82–4, 87, 90, 91, 93, 122, 123, 158, 159, 196, 210, 211, 244, 246, 247, 255, 284, 285, 288, 290, 299, 331, 363
Equal groups 32, 84, 90, 93
Partial products 378, 379, 413
Patterns 25, 164, 165, 247
Properties
Associative (double and halve) 382, 383, 393
Commutative (turnaround) 26, 27, 33, 36, 37, 82, 83, 87, 91, 93, 95, 97, 122–5, 161, 197, 244–7, 249, 286, 336, 366, 374, 457
Distributive (partial products) 378, 379, 413
Related to division 30, 31, 122, 123, 130–5, 137–9, 143, 175, 181, 187, 193, 208–11, 260, 282–5, 288–90, 293, 298, 299, 331, 348, 363, 369, 386, 412
Symbol 24

© ORIGO Education